Then and Now

Then and Now

A Photographic History of Vegetation Change in the Central Great Basin Desert

by

Garry F. Rogers

UNIVERSITY OF UTAH PRESS

SALT LAKE CITY

Library of Congress Cataloging in Publication Data

Rogers, Garry F., 1946-
   Then and now.

   Bibliography: p.
   Includes indexes.
   1. Vegetation dynamics--Great Basin--History--
Pictorial works. 2. Botany--Great Basin--Ecology--
History--Pictorial works. 3. Great Basin--History--
Pictorial works. I. Title. II. Title: Vegetation change
in the central Great Basin Desert. III. Title: Great
Basin Desert.
QK141.R63   581.979   82-4825
ISBN 0-87480-206-7   AACR2

Contents

Figures

Foreword

Many of the problems associated with the study of vegetation change stem from our lack of knowledge about conditions prior to settlement and the introduction of grazing in the past century. Written records are scant, and those available tend to be difficult to interpret because of their subjectivity. Most photographs taken before settlement have been lost, and very few are available from the first two decades after settlement. Because of these limitations, we will probably never know the precise nature of presettlement vegetation. The question may have become unimportant anyway. As pointed out by several students of change in the Great Basin (e.g., Young et al. 1971), presettlement conditions may represent a meaningless standard. During the past century numerous species of annual weeds have been introduced to the Great Basin Desert from other parts of the world. These weeds often defeat native species in the struggle for survival, and as their numbers have grown, they have permanently altered the composition of native vegetation. This situation in no way reduces our responsibility to learn the nature of changes occurring today. In fact, the task has become even more necessary because of the acceleration of change and degradation associated with the introduced weeds.

This book makes a contribution to our knowledge of historical vegetation change. Matched pairs of historical and recent photographs are used to provide examples of some of the changes that have occurred. A more detailed presentation would fill several volumes, and would still be incomplete. I contend that so little is known of actual changes at most locations that a major task facing managers and scientists today is the observation and description of the changes. This is not to say that generalizations should be avoided. In fact, several theoretical contributions have been made in recent years that may apply to the changes illustrated by the matched photographs (see White 1979, Slatyer 1977, Van Hulst 1978, Noble and Slatyer 1977, 1980, Grime 1979, Westoby 1980). A real problem exists in applying the theories to Great Basin vegetation, however, because of the lack of observational data with which to test them.

The process of relocating an old camera station and viewing the changes that have occurred since the original photograph was taken is intriguing. There is a sense of discovery and excitement as the old scene comes into perspective that is completely absorbing. As explained in the section on methods, the requirements for the work are modest. Old photographs are readily available from numerous sources, almost any camera will produce a match, and no special training is required to spot the major changes or lack of changes in the shrubs, trees, and other plants present in the scene. The result is a glimpse of natural history that can be acquired in no other way.

Department of Geography   Garry F. Rogers
Columbia University
May 1981

Acknowledgments

Much of what is interesting and valuable in this book can be attributed to the suggestions and assistance provided by friends and colleagues. Raymond M. Turner loaned copies of many of the original photographs and earlier matches, greatly simplifying my search for old photographs, and reducing the time required to relocate original camera stations in the field. Among the many others who contributed, I would particularly like to thank Donald R. Currey, Walter P. Cottam, and my wife Denise for their help and encouragement throughout the project. At one time or another most of the ecologists, land managers, museums, historical societies, and libraries in and around the Great Basin Desert were consulted for information or suggestions. Many responded, but in particular, James Young, Neil West, Paul Tueller, the U.S. Geological Survey Photo Library, the University of Utah Garrett Herbarium, the University of Arizona Herbarium, the Golden Spike National Historic Site, and the University of Utah Geography Department were generous with their assistance. Of the many others who contributed, the following individuals were especially helpful: George Ballard, Rick Dingus, David Doepner, Robert Austin, and Richard Travis. Not all these individuals would agree with the final form or content of my conclusions, and of course they are not responsible for any errors or inconsistencies that may be present. Most of the information included was obtained while I was a Ph.D. candidate at the Geography Department, University of Utah. The maps and figures were drawn by June H. Walton of the University of Utah Geographic Research Laboratories. Specific acknowledgments for each of the original photographs are given in the Appendix.

Then and Now

Introduction

Planning for future use and maintenance of renewable biological resources requires predictions of ecological responses to proposed and current human activities. Historical information about responses to similar activities in the past would often be enlightening, but usually the available information is too limited to provide the needed answers. A shortage of long-term observations of changes in plant and animal populations following disturbances of the natural environment is a major limitation to understanding and managing ecological responses to disturbances. Examples of the consequences of improper resource use are quite common. They include expansion of deserts in much of the arid portion of the world, invasions by undesirable plant and animal species, unexpected fluctuations of big game populations, and many others. An important first step in mitigating or solving some of these problems would be to place greater emphasis on the acquisition and analysis of historical information such as the photographs presented in this book.

In the Great Basin Desert (Fig. 1), overgrazing by domestic livestock and a reduction in forest and range fires that have occurred since settlement during the middle 1800's are believed to have been the causes of widespread change in native plant communities. The nature and extent of the changes have been inferred from comparisons of contemporary conditions with those reported in the journals and records left by early explorers and immigrants and from studies of isolated sites thought to be more or less free of disturbance. Difficulties in interpreting this evidence have resulted in some uncertainty about the state of original conditions and the subsequent changes. The problem is complicated by the fact that the information we do have is from a small number of sites and may not always be applicable to problems at other, apparently similar, sites for which no information is available. For example, we know that much of the original grassland present in Cache Valley during the early 1800's has been transformed into shrubland (Hull and Hull 1974). Thus it is reasonable to expect that grassland could be reestablished by removing the shrubs and replanting grass. At many locations outside Cache Valley shrublands are present today, but there is no guarantee that grassland can be reestablished. Slight variations in climate or soil can alter the likelihood of grass establishment. Not only are environmental conditions likely to be different at different sites, but also the conditions that affect establishment may have changed since the original grassland existed. Competitive annual weeds may reduce the chances for perennial grasses to survive, and the greater abundance of shrubs in surrounding areas may produce such a heavy seed rain that shrubs reappear almost immediately. Efforts to convert shrubland and woodland to grassland have been successful at numerous locations, but in some instances the conversions have not been successful. Either shrubs and trees have rapidly reappeared or weeds have taken over. It seems probable that pure grassland was rare prior to the introduction of livestock grazing. What is more likely is that long-lived perennial grasses grew mixed with shrubs and trees. The problem facing managers today is reestablishing and maintaining grasses without permitting invasion by annuals or other forms of deterioration.

In this study, comparisons of old and new photographs taken from the same camera locations are used to objectively describe vegetation changes that have occurred at a few sites in western Utah. None of the original photographs were taken before settlement, and consequently they provide only limited information about conditions prior to the advent of domestic livestock grazing. The information they do contain, however, makes it possible to observe the nature of changes that occur under contemporary conditions of continuous grazing. The dates of the original photographs range from 1868 to 1916, and

3

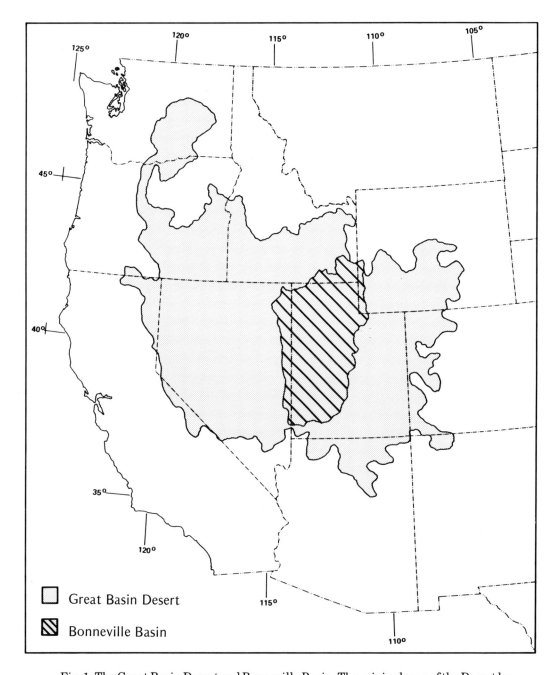

Fig. 1. The Great Basin Desert and Bonneville Basin. The original map of the Desert by Shreve (1942) is here redrawn using information from the U.S. vegetation map by Kuchler (1964). Shreve's boundary has been expanded to include adjacent areas of sagebrush steppe on Kuchler's map. Numerous mountain ranges occur within the boundaries drawn here. Although the mountains are too moist to be considered part of the Desert, they are too numerous to conveniently include in a map of this scale. Use of the term "desert" is not intended to imply the region is truly barren. It is actually quite lush in comparison to large sections of the Asian deserts occuring at similar latitudes.

the dates of the recent photographs range from 1968 to 1980. A summary of the changes they show is provided in the later section entitled Results.

Matched pairs of historical and recent photographs provide a clear record of variations at a particular site and have been used in numerous studies of vegetation change (for examples see Christensen 1957, Hastings and Turner 1965, Gruell 1980, Turner and Karpiscak 1980, and U.S. Bureau of Land Management 1980). In preparation for this study, a large number of photographs taken between 1868 and 1925 were acquired from numerous collections. Initial plans called for matching photographs throughout the Desert, and so photographs were sought from all parts of the region, ranging from New Mexico to Oregon. By chance, however, a large portion of the photographs obtained during the first year of the search was concentrated in western Utah, a region often considered in previous studies and discussions of change (e.g., Cottam 1976). Soon it became apparent that more photographs were available than could possibly be matched in the time allowed for the study. This consideration, and the fortunate discovery of a large number of recently matched photograph pairs from western Utah and southern Idaho, led to the decision to restrict the study to the Bonneville Basin region of central and western Utah, southern Idaho, and eastern Nevada. The recently matched photographs were generously made available by Raymond M. Turner of the U.S. Geological Survey. The matches had been made in 1968 and 1969 at the start of a study being conducted by James Rodney Hastings and Turner. That study was discontinued before the start of my project.

At present over 400 photographs have been matched in the Bonneville Basin by myself, Turner, and Ralph R. Woolley, who matched photographs during the late 1930's and 1940's. Because of the similarity between many scenes and because of limitations on the length of this volume, the decision was made to include only a representative sample of the photographs. Forty-nine sets of two or three matches (referred to as plates) were chosen to illustrate changes at sites scattered throughout the study region. They are presented in four sections and illustrate changes in (1) valley floors dominated by the most drought-tolerant shrubs and herbs, (2) upper valleys and foothills dominated by big sagebrush (*Artemisia tridentata* Nutt.) varieties, (3) upper valleys and foothills with Utah juniper [*Juniperus osteosperma* (Torr.) Little], and (4) upper valleys and foothills near the eastern margin of the Basin dominated by Gambel oak (*Quercus gambelii* Nutt.) and bigtooth maple (*Acer grandidentatum* Nutt. in T. & G.). [Scientific names of plants are given in parentheses only on first mention of the species. Thereafter the common name is used alone. Both names are provided in the Plant Index. Scientific names are based on the works by Arnow and Wyckoff (1977) and Holmgren and Reveal (1966).] These plants often occur together; sagebrush, for example, usually occurs with juniper and with oak and maple. Consequently, the changes illustrated in each of the four sections frequently relate to changes in other sections as well.

THE STUDY REGION

Introduction

A variety of factors may be used to delimit and characterize a region of the Earth's surface. Geomorphic differences are often quite striking; no doubt exists that the Great Plains and Rocky Mountains are different, but many times less obvious factors create important differences. Possible sources of distinction include soils, climate, plant and animal life, and, increasingly, the characteristics of human occupation. The name Great Basin, however, comes from yet another characteristic of the environment—the nature of surface-water drainage systems.

On May 24, 1844, John C. Frémont reached Utah Lake (Fig. 2), having finally completed an exploration of the region bordered by the Wasatch Mountains of central Utah on the east, the Sierra Nevada Mountains of eastern California to the west, the Snake River Plains of southern Idaho in the north, and the Mojave Desert to the south. For some time there had been reports of a navigable river flowing from the vicinity of Great Salt Lake to the Pacific Ocean. Frémont found, however, that the entire region was one of interior drainage having "... no communication with the sea" [this phrase appeared on a map entitled "Map of an Exploring Expedition to the Rocky Mountains in 1842 and to Oregon and North California in the Years 1843–44" (Cline 1963:215)]—truly a great basin. The Great Basin is the largest of several areas of interior drainage in the United States and contains within its boundaries a number of separate basins, one of which is the Bonneville Basin of western Utah (Hunt 1974).

The Bonneville Basin was named for Benjamin

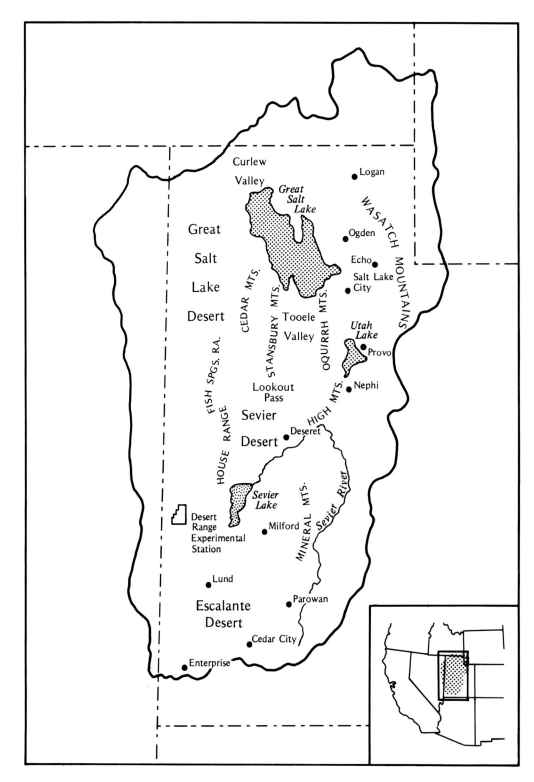

Fig. 2. Some place-names referred to in the text.

Bonneville, a U.S. Army officer who explored sections of the Great Basin, including the region around Great Salt Lake, during the years 1832–35. In 1837 Washington Irving published a book on the subject of Bonneville's explorations, and on a map included in the book Salt Lake was labeled Lake Bonneville. It is possible that the naming of Pleistocene Lake Bonneville, which formerly occupied most of the valleys of western Utah, and of which Great Salt Lake is only a remnant, was influenced by this map (Cline 1963).

Physical Geography

It has been shown in previous research that a strong association exists between general climatic variables and vegetation identified by a few dominant life forms or species (e.g., Mather and Yoshioka 1966). Climate of the Great Basin is strongly influenced by the Basin's high elevation and rain shadow position between the Sierra Nevada Mountains that block Pacific moisture and the Rocky Mountains that cut off Gulf of Mexico moisture. Within the Basin stretching and faulting of the lithosphere has produced numerous linear mountain ranges perpendicular to the direction of stretching. These northerly trending mountains are separated by wide valleys with floors mostly above 1370 m (4500 ft). Many of the valleys have no external drainage systems under current climatic conditions, and their floors are often covered by flat-bedded "playas" occasionally occupied by ephemeral lakes. One of the largest playas in the Basin, the Great Salt Lake Desert, occurs in the central Bonneville Basin to the west of Great Salt Lake (Fig. 2). Periodic innundation and evaporation has produced extensive salt deposits called salt pans in many lower valley floors. Saline soils coupled with low precipitation amounts and high temperatures often create conditions too extreme for even the hardiest plants, and extensive areas devoid of plant life are found in some valleys.

The Bonneville Basin occupies the eastern third of the Great Basin (Fig. 1) and includes most of the western half of Utah. Within the Basin, valley elevations range from about 1585 m (5200 ft) in the Escalante Desert (Fig. 2) to about 1280 m (4200 ft) at the Great Salt Lake. Steep mountain slopes cover about one fourth of the Basin, and more gently sloping gravel fans occupy about one third. The remaining surface area is taken up by nearly level basin floors. During the Pleistocene epoch a large portion of the Basin was occupied by Lake Bonneville, a large freshwater lake approximately the size of Lake Michigan. Consequently, lake-bottom sediments occupy most of the valley floors, and extensive remnant beaches appear at various heights above the valleys.

Dominant plants of the Bonneville Basin tend to be tolerant of a range of soil characteristics. Vest (1962), in his study conducted at the southern end of the Great Salt Lake Desert, found that available soil moisture was the most important soil factor accounting for abrupt vegetational boundaries. Skougard (1976), however, found that the distribution of plants in the Goshen Playa south of Utah Lake was influenced more by amounts of soluble salts than soil moisture. Visual comparison of Foster's vegetation map (Foster 1968) with the "General Soil Map of Utah" (Soil Conservation Survey 1973) gives an impression of general relationships, but close agreements between soil and vegetation boundaries are not present. A similar lack of close correlation is reported by Gates and his colleagues (1956) in their study of soils and vegetation at several locations throughout the Basin. Part of the difficulty in specifying a relationship stems from the wide tolerances of many of the dominant species, several of which extend far beyond the Bonneville Basin to regions of both different soils and different climates.

Climate. Climatic constraints on plant growth in the Great Basin Desert are partially a result of the great variability of precipitation and temperature. In the Bonneville Basin, annual temperature extremes range from well below freezing to over 38° C (100° F). At Milford, a mid-elevation valley location (1532 m, 5028 ft) near the south end of the Basin, a low temperature of −33° C (−28° F) was recorded in January 1953, and a high temperature of 40° C (105° F) was recorded in June 1955. Wide annual fluctuations are matched by wide daily variations. High temperature due to rapid soil heating during the day falls rapidly at night as heat is radiated back into the dry desert air.

Moisture. Precipitation in the Bonneville Basin is influenced by several factors. In the westernmost portion (Fig. 3), rainfall in May and October is associated with the development of closed low-pressure centers aloft which produce upward movement of surface air, adiabatic cooling, and occasionally heavy rainfall (Jeppson et al. 1968). This precipitation is not strongly associated with topography and may be as likely to occur over a valley as in foothills or mountains. The slight peak in precipitation in August in the western section results from thunderstorms. In this case rainfall is often associated with topography—increasing with elevation—but may also result when convectional cells form as air heated near the ground surface rises through cooler air above.

In the north-central section (Fig. 3) precipitation results primarily from frontal storms occurring during the winter and from combined frontal and low aloft activity in April. Frontal storms typically develop in the Gulf of Alaska and sweep across the region from the northwest. Winter precipitation in the eastern portion of the Bonneville Basin is mainly frontal. The south-central section receives precipitation from winter fronts, thunderstorms in August, and lows aloft in October.

The probability of receiving precipitation at different times of the year is closely related to the total annual amount received. In general, the probability of precipitation is greatest in winter, but significant peaks in probability occur in mid-summer to the south (Fig. 4).

Temperature. Ordinarily, temperature in the Desert decreases with increase in elevation. The average rate of decrease is about .6° C per 100 m (3.3° F per 1000 ft). Frequently, however, rapidly cooling air at high elevations flows downslope at night producing an upward displacement of warm valley air. As a result temperature fluctuations are often greater in lower valleys than in upper valleys and adjacent foothills. A consequence that may be important to plant distribution is illustrated in Fig. 5 which shows that the number of days with temperatures below freezing can be greater in lower valleys than adjacent upper valleys and foothills. Because of the stabilizing influence of the large body of water contained in Great Salt Lake, many valleys surrounding the lake do not experience these temperature inversions as strongly as valleys elsewhere in the Basin.

Evapotranspiration. Attempts have been made to estimate climatic stress on plants by assessing plant responses to variations in temperature. A popular index of stress is potential evapotranspiration (PE). PE is an estimate of the combined potential for water loss from plants and non-plant surfaces. The term potential is applied because the heat energy available for evaporating water may exceed the quantity of water actually present. Inadequate moisture supplies are experienced during the summer months at all valley locations in the Bonneville Basin. Although cool air drainage may produce cooler night-time temperatures, daytime temperatures are sufficiently higher in valleys than surrounding foothills to produce greater overall PE in lower valley locations. In the Basin, annual PE ranges from about 84 cm (33 in) over most of the Great Salt Lake Desert to about 51 cm (20 in) in the foothills. PE at higher elevations is less.

Some soil moisture usually accumulates in the valleys during the winter, but most of it is exhausted sometime between April 1 and about mid-June (Jeppson et al. 1968). Thereafter plants must depend on the infrequent occurrence of summer rainfall. Winter precipitation amounts exceed summer amounts throughout the Basin. The mid-summer peak to the south (Fig. 4), however, may account for the persistence of perennial grasslands in the Escalante Desert. This is because of the greater ability of grasses to take advantage of sporadic summer rainfall (Gleason and Cronquist 1964:252).

Vegetation. Plant communities of the Great Basin Desert have been described in numerous previous publications. Descriptions encompassing most or all of the Desert include those by Shreve (1942), Cronquist et al. (1972), Shantz (1925), Sampson (1925), McGinnies (1968), MacMahon (1979), and Harper and Reveal (1978). A detailed map has been prepared of the State of Utah by Foster (1968) at a scale of 1:500,000. The following discussion consists of a brief introduction to vegetation appearing in the matched photographs. The units of vegetation described are defined primarily by the dominance of single species. The references cited above should be consulted by those wishing additional information.

The visual character of Bonneville Basin vegetation is usually determined by one or a few species. The similarity of the forms of these species, their pale colors, and their often sparse distribution, tend to produce impressions of monotonous desolation among those unfamiliar with this vegetation (Reveal 1979). Lower valleys are indeed often quite barren, and bare soil may dominate the scene.

1. Lower valley communities. Iodine bush [*Allenrolfea occidentalis* (Wats.) Kuntze] dominated communities occur on the margins of playas throughout the study region. Large communities occur in the Great Salt Lake Desert and small communities are found in the Sevier Desert and Escalante Desert to the south. Principal shrubs associated with iodine bush include red samphire (*Salicornia europaea* L.), mound saltbrush [*Atriplex falcata* (M. E. Jones) Standl.], saltgrass [*Distichlis spicata* (L.) Greene],

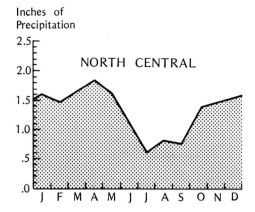

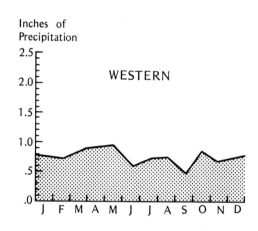

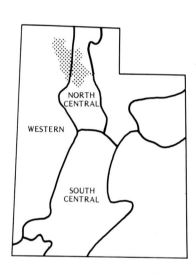

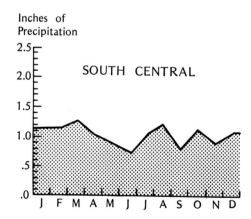

Fig. 3. Average monthly precipitation for natural climatic zones in Utah (from Jeppson et al. 1968).

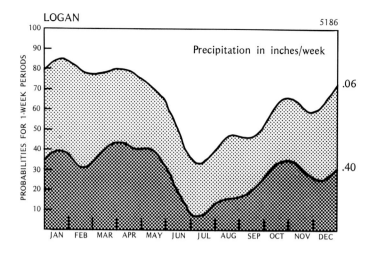

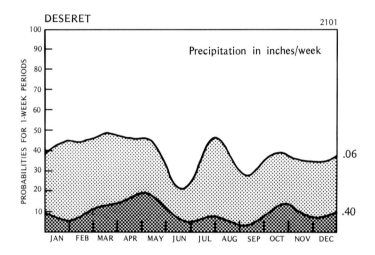

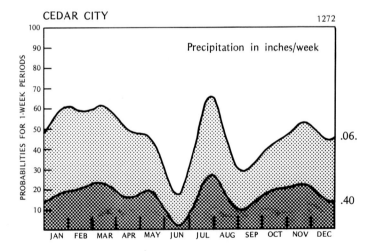

Fig. 4. Precipitation probabilities for three Bonneville Basin weather stations. The curves show the probability of receiving measurable precipitation (.06 in or more) or appreciable precipitation (.40 in) during any given week. In any seven-day period in October, Deseret will receive .40 in or more only about one year in ten (from Jeppson et al. 1968).

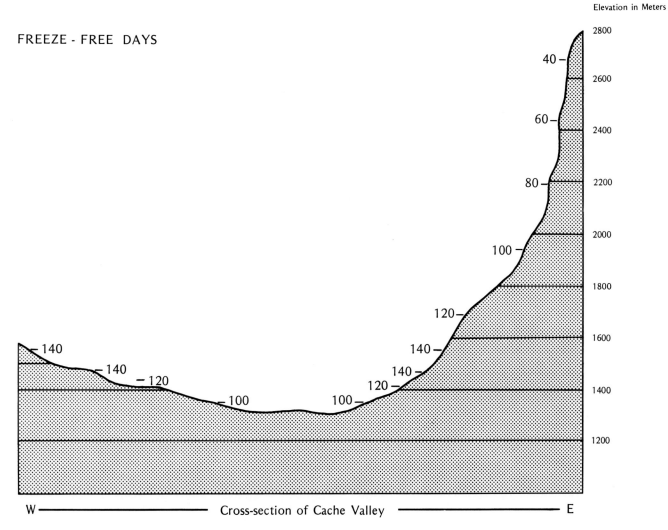

Fig. 5. Number of freeze-free days in Cache Valley, Utah. Valley floor locations at 1370 m (4493 ft) and foothill locations at 1980 m (6493 ft) both have about 100 days each year during which temperatures do not fall below 0° C (32° F). Sites at altitudes between these have a longer frost-free period (redrawn from Jeppson et al. 1968).

greasewood [*Sarcobatus vermiculatus* (Hook) Torr.], Utah samphire (*Salicornia utahensis* Tides.), seepweed (*Suaeda torreyana* Wats.), and alkali sacaton [*Sporobolus airoides* (Torr.) Torr. var. *airoides*]. Numerous species of small annuals are usually present and can be found growing at the bases of the shrubs or sometimes carpeting the ground. Most of the annuals are recent introductions to the region.

Meadows dominated by saltgrass, a pale green perennial grass, often alternate with shrub communities dominated by iodine bush. The species listed above that are found with iodine bush also grow with saltgrass but are usually very scattered or are restricted to margins of saltgrass meadows. Saltgrass communities are found near Great Salt Lake, near the western and southern margins of Great Salt Lake Desert, around the south end of Utah Lake, and in the Escalante Desert. A saltgrass meadow can be seen in the left center of the recent photograph in Plate 1.

Lower reaches of the gravel fans and pediments ascending from valley floors are dominated by shadscale [*Atriplex confertifolia* (Torr. & Frem.) Wats.]. A number of other shrubs occur with shadscale in mixed stands dominated by one or several species in a zone surrounding the more salt-tolerant communities described above. Shadscale is the most common species, and this vegetation, which occurs throughout the Bonneville Basin, is often referred to collectively as the shadscale zone. Common annual species, often dominant over large areas, include cheatgrass (*Bromus tectorum* L.), halogeton (*Halogeton glomeratus* C. A. Mey. in Ledeb.), bur buttercup (*Ranunculus testiculatus* Crantz), and numerous others (see Fig. 6).

Communities dominated by the deciduous shrub greasewood are somewhat transitional between the valley floor communities and the shadscale zone. Greasewood is phreatophytic, dependent on ground water, and is quite variable in size depending on local habitat conditions. Seepweed, saltgrass, iodine bush, and other species mentioned above may occur with greasewood. Though not as extensive as shadscale, greasewood communities are scattered throughout the Bonneville Basin. The appearance of this vegetation is illustrated by Plates 1, 6, and 12.

Green molly summercypress (*Kochia americana* Wats.), a small shrub occurring throughout the shadscale zone, was formerly a frequent dominant (e.g., Shantz and Piemeisel 1940), but today is less common and occurs mainly on clay playas or in the lower

portions of the shadscale community (Foster 1968:59). Illustrations of this vegetation are provided by the original photographs of Plates 2 and 3.

Horsebrush (*Tetradymia canescens* DC.) dominated communities are found near the Thomas Range, west of the Fish Springs Range, near the Confusion Range, and near the Cricket Mountains. Common associates include shadscale, little rabbitbrush [*Chrysothamnus viscidiflorus* (Hook.) Nutt.], galleta [*Hilaria jamesii* (Torr.) Benth.], Mormon tea (*Ephedra* L.), Indian ricegrass [*Oryzopsis hymenoides* (R. & S.) Ricker in Piper], and winterfat [*Eurotia lanata* (Pursh) Moq.]. Horsebrush appears in Plates 8, 9, 10, and in lesser amounts in several others. A horsebrush plant that may be over 60 years old is present in the lower right of both photographs in Plate 26.

Like green molly summercypress, winterfat appears to be less common now than it was a century ago. Currently winterfat dominated communities occur northwest of Great Salt Lake, near Sevier Lake, and in the Escalante Desert. Common associates include Indian ricegrass, galleta, little rabbitbrush, and sagebrush. A winterfat dominated community appears in Plate 13.

Little rabbitbrush communities are dominated by two similar species of *Chrysothamnus*, both of which may be varieties of *viscidiflorus* (Hook.) Nutt. These communities sometimes alternate with winterfat and are associated with many of the same species. Snakeweed [*Xanthocephalum sarothrae* (Pursh) Shinners], a small semishrub, is often found sharing dominance with little rabbitbrush. In the Bonneville Basin these communities occur primarily in the Escalante Desert. An illustration of a little rabbitbrush community mixed with galleta is provided by Plate 21.

2. Upper valley and foothills with sagebrush and juniper. Vegetation above the shadscale zone is dominated by big sagebrush. Sagebrush is an evergreen shrub with small gray-green leaves and shaggy bark. Mark Twain gives an imaginative description of sagebrush vegetation, picturing it as a miniature forest in which gnats appear as lilliputian birds (Twain 1899:30-34). As noted by Twain, few other plants grow with sagebrush, with the exception of bunchgrass. Common bunchgrass species in the Bonneville Basin include bluebunch wheatgrass [*Agropyron spicatum* (Pursh) Scribn. & Sm.], Sandburg bluegrass (*Poa secunda* Presl), needlegrass (*Stipa comata* Trin. & Rupr.), and sand dropseed [*Spor-*

Fig. 6. A pure stand of halogeton on Fish Springs Flat east of the Fish Springs Range. Darker plants are the current year's growth. Photograph: September 14, 1976, Rogers No. 18–N.

obolus cryptandrus (Torr.) Gray]. Twain mistakenly compared sagebrush wood to that of oak. Sagebrush is very brittle, and in heavily grazed areas the plants are often damaged by trampling and dead branches may litter the ground.

Sagebrush communities in the Bonneville Basin are dominated by varieties of big sagebrush in most locations, but black sagebrush (*Artemisia arbuscula* Nutt.) dominates rocky ridges and slopes, often in association with species common to the shadscale zone. The bunchgrasses listed above are usually present in low quantities, but cheatgrass and other annuals are frequently abundant. Several shrub species, including little rabbitbrush, snakeweed, shadscale, and winterfat, are sometimes present, and rubber rabbitbrush [*Chrysothamnus nauseosus* (Pall.) Britt. in Britt. & Br.] occasionally dominates small areas. More detailed descriptions of sagebrush vegetation are provided by Beetle (1979), Vale (1973), West (1979b), and Young et al. (1979). A number of the plates illustrate sagebrush vegetation, and Fig. 7 shows the sagebrush band occurring on the east side of Skull Valley.

Grasslands occurring within the sagebrush community tend to be dominated by annuals, chiefly cheatgrass (see Fig. 8), except for those dominated by galleta in the Escalante Desert. Common annuals include Russian thistle (*Salsola kali* L.), storksbill [*Erodium cicutarium* (L.) L'Hér. ex Ait.], and Belvedere summercypress [*Kochia scoparia* (L.) Schrad.], to name but a few. Foster (1968) lists a few locations in the Bonneville Basin where bunchgrasses are abundant.

Above the sagebrush band, and sometimes intergrading with it or even replacing it, occurs a band of woodland dominated by Utah juniper. Pinyon (*Pinus edulis* Engelm. and *P. monophylla* Torr. & Frem.) often occurs mixed with juniper, but this is usually at higher altitudes, and it is not well represented by any of the matched photographs. The width of the sagebrush and juniper bands varies considerably and either may be entirely absent. A distinct sagebrush band is absent on the west slope of the Cedar Mountains where juniper intergrades with shadscale and sagebrush occurs mainly as an understory species in the juniper woodland. At other locations, particularly on the western slopes of the lower and narrower basin ranges, the sagebrush band is quite narrow.

Descriptions of the juniper woodland are provided by Beeson (1974), Foster (1968), Woodbury (1947), West et al. (1978), and Tueller et al. (1979). Several bibliographies containing many additional references are also available (Aldon and Springfield 1973, West et al. 1973). The woodland is illustrated by Plates 26-38, and Fig. 7.

3. Upper valleys and foothills with oak and maple. Along the eastern margin of the Bonneville Basin, in the Wasatch Mountains, and in limited sections of the nearby Basin ranges to the west, Gambel oak in a matrix of sagebrush, grasses, and forbs takes the place of juniper. Bigtooth maple is common but is generally restricted to moist sites in ravines and on north-facing slopes. Small stands of juniper are present in the Wasatch Mountains, but only south of Utah Lake do they become nearly as abundant as oak and maple. In the northern half of the Wasatch Range oak disappears and maple becomes the dominant. General descriptions of the flora, fauna, and environment of this vegetation may be found in Allman (1953), Hayward (1948), Ream (1960, 1963), and Wilcox (1977). The work by Cronquist et al. (1972) contains a good general review.

Animal life. A factor of great importance to considerations of vegetation change is the relationship between plants and the animals that depend on them for food and shelter. Knowledge of the animals inhabiting the Great Basin Desert is extensive in comparison to what is known of similar deserts in other parts of the world (McGinnies 1968), but our understanding of most features of their existence of significance to plants in the Great Basin is limited. The information available is often no more than a list of species normally found within a particular plant community. In the Bonneville Basin descriptive information is provided by Fautin (1946), Vest (1962), and Montgomery (1976) for lower valley shrub communities, by Frischknecht (1975) for upper valley and foothill woodlands, and Hayward (1948) for oak and maple communities of the Wasatch Mountains. The more general works by Durrant (1952), Harper and Reveal (1978), and Zohner (1967) contain additional information. Some examples of animal induced changes are given at the end of the next section.

The Literature of Change

Vegetation. Previous publications have described historical changes in virtually all vegetation of the Bonneville Basin. Most of the studies have reported increases in shrubs or trees, or both, but many also report a widespread increase of introduced annual

Fig. 7. A fire scar in the transition zone between juniper and sagebrush. The fire scar is the lighter patch in the upper center where the juniper woodland (foreground) intergrades with sagebrush shrubland (medium tone). The view is west across Skull Valley from the west slope of the Stansbury Mountains. Photograph: September 3, 1976, Rogers No. 13–N.

weed species. Most of the research has been conducted in the more productive upper-valley and foothill sites. Studies of change in the sparsely vegetated valley floors have been fewer in number, and comparatively little information is available.

In the lowest valley areas vegetation change is often induced by accumulations of runoff water in temporary lakes, by fluctuations of groundwater levels, and by fluctuations of water levels in permanent lakes. Two large permanent lakes, Utah Lake and Great Salt Lake, occur in the northern portion of the Basin, and formerly permanent Sevier Lake, now intermittent because of water diversion from the Sevier River for agriculture, occurs in the south. Ephemeral playa lakes occur in numerous valleys. Changes associated with lake-level fluctuations have been observed, or deduced, from the arrangement of contemporary plant communities surrounding the lakes. Sequences for Great Salt Lake are described by Flowers (1934), and those for Utah Lake by Cottam (1926).

In the study by Flowers, concentric zones of plants surrounding the margins of Great Salt Lake and neighboring playas were carefully described and related to various characteristics of soil and moisture conditions. Flowers assumed that the communities occurring closest to the water formed the early succession communities that would gradually move inward following sedimentation of the lake or following lowering of the water level. Flowers found that a variety of sequences was possible. Although only a few plant species tended to colonize barren mud flats, the communities that formed after the initial colonization were composed of nearly all combinations of the salt-tolerant species growing in the region. The principal colonists were samphire and iodine bush; intermediate stages were composed of combinations of saltgrass, seepweed, alkali sacaton, rabbitbrush, saltbush (*Atriplex* L.) species, green molly summercypress, winterfat, greasewood, and shadscale. Greasewood and shadscale tended to occur later in the succession and were followed by sagebrush or mixed shrub and bunchgrass communities.

Flowers' observations were quite detailed but were conducted over a relatively short time period, and his inferences about species exchanges through time have received little confirmation from additional studies. The rates of change are unknown, and so it is impossible to predict changes that will occur during intervals of lake level fluctuation or similar forms of disturbance. Predictions are further complicated by

the interchangeability of many of the species in the succession. "They occur in nearly every combination as the intermediate successional state" (Flowers 1934:413).

Human disturbance is probably least in the lower valley communities than in any other vegetation in the study region. Livestock grazing occurs, but soils are generally too saline for agricultural use, and the scattered nature of the vegetation is not conducive to fire spread. As with other communities, however, introduced annuals are common. Although studies of the spread of these species have mostly been conducted in locations above the valley floors, it was observed during the course of fieldwork that several species are quite abundant, often occupying playa sites unoccupied by native species. Halogeton, for example, occurs in extensive stands in parts of the Great Salt Lake Desert, the Escalante Desert, and elsewhere (see Fig. 6). Although invasions by these species may be lamented for some reasons (halogeton is poisonous to livestock), where they occur in previously unoccupied portions of the habitat they at least do not replace native species.

Plant communities found in the shadscale zone surrounding the valley floors are more extensive and productive. Plant communities in this zone are important as winter livestock range, particularly for sheep, and support the winter food requirements of several million animals throughout the Desert. Ecological studies such as those by Flowers (1934), Kearney et al. (1914), and Cottam (1976) contain some information about changes in this zone, but the most detailed studies have been concerned primarily with the response of the vegetation to livestock grazing. Changes associated with grazing have been studied at the Desert Range Experiment Station in the southern end of the Bonneville Basin since 1933 (Harper 1959, Holmgren 1975, Holmgren and Hutchings 1972, Hutchings and Stewart 1953, Norton 1978, West 1979a), in Curlew Valley near the north end of the Basin, and elsewhere for varying periods (Shantz and Piemeisel 1940, Stewart et al. 1940, Currie 1963, Child 1970, Cook 1977, Rice and Westoby 1978, West and Gasto 1978).

Most of these studies have used fenced plots to control the intensity and timing of grazing. At the Desert Range Experiment Station, repeated observations have been made of vegetation response to grazing of light, moderate, and heavy intensity occurring at six different times during the winter. In some studies (e.g., Child 1970) plant responses have been evaluated following artificial clipping to simulate grazing.

There have been mixed results from these studies. Early reports (e.g., Harper 1959) indicated that palatable species declined with grazing. Child (1970), for example, found that shadscale, winterfat, and other species did not recover their original size even after seven years following being clipped, regardless of season and frequency of clipping. In recent studies, however, analysis of longevity of individual plants, and a study of changes in quantities of several species, have shown there to be little discernible difference between sites with, or without, livestock grazing (Norton 1978, Rice and Westoby 1978, West 1979a).

Studies of change in sagebrush communities have been numerous (e.g., Anderson and Holte 1981). In general, it has been concluded that perennial grasses that formerly occurred in varying densities with sagebrush have been practically eradicated by livestock grazing. As grasses have declined sagebrush has increased. In a review of 19 studies of ungrazed or lightly grazed protected areas, Vale (1973) concluded that there had been an increase in sagebrush on unprotected rangelands throughout the region dominated by the species, including the northern portion of the Great Basin Desert.

At the present time sagebrush is gradually being replaced by short-lived, introduced annuals (see Fig. 8). Annual species have long been important in the Great Basin as colonists of disturbed areas, but in recent years their increasing abundance and the greater fire hazard they produce has tended to intensify fire frequency to the point that sagebrush can no longer become established (Young et al. 1971, West 1979b). The introduced annuals are well adapted to frequent disturbance. They produce abundant small seeds that are readily dispersed, and they reach reproductive maturity in a single season.

Piemeisel (1951) conducted intensive studies of the behavior of annuals during the years immediately following abandonment of farmland in southern Idaho. On areas of similar soil, without outside disturbances such as grazing, the first species to occupy bare ground was Russian thistle (*Salsola kali* var. *tenuiflora* Tausch.). Russian thistle maintained dominance for about two years during which time three other species of annuals appeared and increased in number. Two mustards [*Descurainia sophia* (L.) Webb and *Sisymbrium altissimum* L.] superseded Russian thistle in importance during the third year

and were replaced in turn by cheatgrass during the fifth. "Each spread at their particular rate and much as if the preceding stage was not there. This is of course literally true of Russian thistle since it spreads over unoccupied ground, and nearly as true for mustards since they spread into former Russian thistle areas and start to grow in fall when Russian thistle is represented not by living plants but only by dried plants and seed. The two do not enter into competition until the following spring and by that time the mustards are well-grown whereas Russian thistle must establish itself as a seedling, a very unequal competition" (Piemeisel 1951:67). Because of crowding after the second year, Russian thistle produced very little seed, and seedlings that resulted did not survive. Cheatgrass replaced the mustards, even though beginning growth at the same time, because it grew more rapidly.

Piemeisel observed that the replacement of one community by another was largely a response to available moisture and the efficiency of its use by each species. Annual variation in precipitation was less important than plant density in affecting the availability of moisture. Regarding the order of appearance of the species, Piemeisel concluded, "The community first on the ground is there because of its rapid migration and development and the second, because of its greater capacity to hold the ground once it gets there" (1951:67).

One of the earliest studies of change involving juniper was conducted in Mountain Meadow Valley at the south end of the Bonneville Basin (Cottam 1929, Cottam and Stewart 1940). From several sources of historical information, Cottam and Stewart concluded that heavy grazing after 1864 led to plant cover depletion resulting in rapid runoff and flooding following exceptionally heavy rains in 1884. The flooding eroded a deep wash through the meadow lowering the water table and eventually leading to elimination of the wet-meadow vegetation of the central valley area. Continued heavy grazing led to replacement of remaining valley and foothill grasses with Russian thistle, sagebrush, rubber rabbitbrush, and juniper. At the time of the study juniper had spread from its former position on ridge tops to most of the valley sides and parts of the valley floor. The authors concluded that juniper had not spread across the entire valley floor because of competition from dense stands of sagebrush, and because of repeated burning of some areas occupied by rabbitbrush. Whether or not juniper finally invaded the valley

Fig. 8. Vegetation within the fire scar visible in Fig. 7. The scene is composed of a mosaic of Russian thistle (foreground), cheatgrass (left center and center), and patches of sagebrush skipped by the fire (band of shrubs beyond the cheatgrass). Dead juniper are present in the upper left (just beyond the sagebrush skip), and two fire-killed sagebrush are present at right center. Photograph: September 3, 1976, Rogers No. 14–N.

floor is uncertain. Additional studies have not been conducted, and during the 1950's part of the developing woodland was cleared in an effort to increase grass production.

Near the center of the Bonneville Basin, Barney and Frischknecht (1974) conducted a study of vegetation changes taking place following fires in juniper woodland. Their study included 28 sites that had been burned from 3 to over 100 years ago. The authors assumed that the vegetation present on separate burns of varying age represented the vegetation that would develop on an individual site. Thus they combined the data from all 28 burns in a single hypothetical sequence (Fig. 9). In this sequence annual species appearing shortly after a fire were gradually replaced by perennial grasses. The grasses achieved dominance within about 5 years. Thereafter, sagebrush steadily invaded and became dominant within about 35 years after the fire. Juniper increased slowly for the first 45 years after which it increased rapidly and sagebrush declined. Juniper cover increased to over 30% in 100 years, and the combined cover of grasses and sagebrush dropped to less than 10%. What appear to be similar sequences occur throughout the Bonneville Basin (see Figs. 7 and 8, and Plate 27).

Upper valleys and foothills with oak are generally thought to have experienced a decline of grass and increase of sagebrush and oak similar to that described above. Numerous studies of change of grasslands and of oak distribution were conducted by the late E. M. Christensen (1949, 1950, 1955, 1957, 1958a, 1958b, 1961, 1962, 1963, 1964a, 1964b). From a variety of historical records, Christensen concluded that oak had expanded considerably since settlement. The expansion was primarily the result of growth of individual clones (multiple stemmed patches). Christensen estimated that the rate of expansion ranged from 4 to 30 cm (1.5 to 12 in) per year, averaging 10 cm (4 in). Christensen's comparison of 1872 photographs with duplicates taken in 1939–40, and 1917–24 photographs with matches made in 1956, suggest that most of the spread occurred after 1900 (see Christensen 1957).

Because of its ability to replace damaged or senescent stems by sprouting, individual oak clones may be capable of persisting for thousands of years. Cottam et al. (1959) report that sterile hybrids originating from natural crossing of Gambel oak and shrub live oak (*Quercus turbinella* Greene) have persisted

at several locations in the study area since the Altithermal (ca. 4000 years before the present). During the Altithermal, the Basin climate was warmer, and the range of shrub live oak extended farther north than at present, overlapping the range of Gambel oak. The hybrids exhibit characteristics of both progenitors, including the greater tolerance to freezes exhibited by Gambel oak. Although unable to produce new plants from seed, the hybrid does produce new stems by sprouting, and thereby has survived a long period of climatic cooling during which shrub live oak was driven south. Northernmost hybrids are now separated from the nearest shrub live oak by a distance of 418 km (260 mi).

Bigtooth maple, often codominant with Gambel oak, is also capable of resprouting after being damaged (Fig. 10). A detailed study of oak-maple vegetation begun in 1948 (Allman 1953, Nixon and Christensen 1959, Nixon 1961, Eastmond 1968) has shown that maple is capable of replacing oak, and several of the matched photos show that maple has increased (Plates 43, 46, and 47).

Animal induced changes. Specific knowledge of the nature and consequences of plant and animal interactions of importance to Bonneville Basin plant communities is available but is usually incomplete. For example, Frischknecht and Baker (1972) report on widespread kill and damage of sagebrush by long-tailed voles (*Microtus longicaudus latus* Hall) during the winter of 1968–69. The authors found the incident to be the result of a rapid vole population increase, but were unable to identify the responsible factors. A similar report is provided by Woodbury (1955) who observed jackrabbit (*Lepus californicus* Gray) population increases in the Bonneville Basin, but was unable to explain their occurrence. Population explosions have been observed in other species of rodents, in insects, and among larger grazing animals, but the frequency with which these events occur and the resultant effects on vegetation are difficult to assess. A possible exception stems from the work of Spencer (1964) conducted on Mesa Verde in Colorado. Spencer found that past porcupine (*Erethizon dorsatum* L.) population explosions were recorded by the growth rings of trees whose bark was eaten by the porcupines. Widespread damage occurred in 1885 and 1935, and minor damage occurred in 1845 and 1905. What appears to be a similar situation is found among the pinyon trees of Red Pine Mountain (Plates 31 and 32). The matched photo-

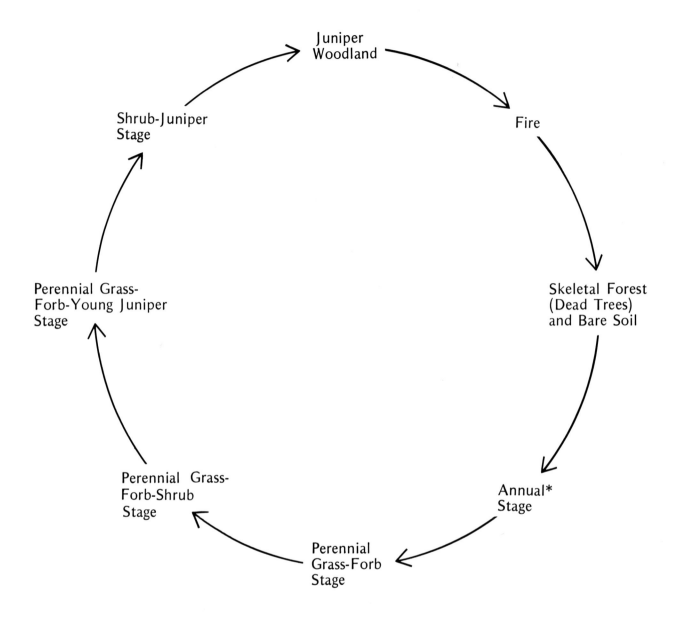

*Could be by-passed to some degree in areas having fair perennial herbaceous cover prior to burning.

Fig. 9. Fire initiated changes in juniper woodland (redrawn from Barney and Frischknecht 1974).

Fig. 10. Bigtooth maple resprouting after a fire. This photograph was taken in the burn visible in the match photograph of Plate 45. Gambel oak (upper right and background) and other bigtooth maple on this slope were resprouting vigorously. Photograph: September 21, 1977, Rogers No. 60–N.

graphs were taken too far from the pinyon stands on the mountain slopes to show changes well, but dead and damaged trees are abundant there.

At the time of settlement in the mid 1800's, it is believed by some that large grazing animals were rare in the Great Basin (Young et al. 1976). During the past several thousand years, widespread extinctions among large mammals are known to have occurred. The extinctions may have been a result of overkill by earlier human inhabitants (Martin 1967) or may have been a result of gradual, climate-induced changes in native plant communities upon which the mammals depended for food (Reveal 1979). Although these changes are considered to have been relatively rapid, they were probably quite slow in comparison to changes brought about by human intervention during the past century and a half. During the period 1825–34, fur trappers harvested large numbers of fur-bearing mammals of the region. The trappers reported the presence of antelope (*Antilocapra americana* Ord), buffalo (*Bison bison*), and deer (*Odocoileus hemionus* Rafinesque), but buffalo were not present when the Mormons arrived in 1847, and by 1900 only small isolated bands of antelope remained (Hull and Hull 1974, John and Bowden 1974, Yoakum 1978). Size of the deer population during the 1800's is uncertain, but current numbers may be much greater than they were around 1900 (Pengelly 1976). Beginning in the late 1800's, numerous species have been introduced to the region. Popov (1949) reported that 42 species of fish and game animals and birds had been introduced into the State of Utah since about 1870.

METHODS

Sources of Old Photographs

Useful historical photographs can be found in museums, libraries, private collections, and other archives. Usually there is little relationship between archival location and the place the original negative was exposed. Occasionally collections of photographs will be found in storage at the place of origin of the photographer. For example, the thousands of negatives by H. L. Shantz are archived in the Herbarium, University of Arizona, where Shantz served as university president for a number of years. The Shantz collection includes numerous scenes from the Bonneville Basin taken between 1908 and 1925. Shantz considered photographs important ecological records

and always included botanical information along with locational and exposure information with each photograph. Despite the usefulness of Shantz's photographs, they have not, to my knowledge, been used in any historical studies of Great Basin ecology.

For research in the western United States the collection of historical photographs maintained by the U.S. Geological Survey Photo Library in Denver, Colorado, is probably the best single source. The Survey's collection is well documented and cataloged and contains many original photographs and negatives. The number of photographs over 50 years old exceeds 10,000 for states of the Great Basin Desert region and includes photographs from as early as the 1860's. Other important general collections include the Library of Congress, National Archives, and Smithsonian Institution. Of steadily increasing importance is the pre-World War II collection of aerial photographs taken between 1929 and 1943 now maintained by the Cartographic Archives Division of the National Archives (Taylor and Spurr 1973). The collection includes large-scale photographs of about 85% of the contiguous United States.

Old photographs of scenes in the Bonneville Basin are relatively abundant compared to other sections of the Desert. Portions of the area north of the Great Salt Lake were photographed extensively in the late 1860's in conjunction with the construction and completion of the first transcontinental railroad, and other areas were photographed by members of the early geographical expeditions and surveys and by photographers making their home in Salt Lake City from about 1855 to 1872. Important early photographers of the Bonneville Basin include Timothy H. O'Sullivan, William H. Jackson, Alfred J. Russell, Charles R. Savage, and George E. Anderson. Several books dealing with the activities of these and other early photographers have become available (Naef and Wood 1975, Wadsworth 1975).

Hundreds of photographs were taken in the Bonneville Basin by the geologist G. K. Gilbert during the summer of 1901. Gilbert's work emphasized the Wasatch Mountains, but extended south and west throughout the entire Bonneville Basin. His photographs of western Utah mountain ranges are numerous, of high quality, and for many locations are the only ones available. Gilbert's concern with structural geology and faulting resulted in emphasis among his photographs on the sagebrush and juniper-dominated upper valley and foothill habitats of the Basin ranges and the oak-dominated foothills of the

Wasatch Mountains. Scenes of lower valley vegetation are infrequent among the Gilbert photographs. The need for scenes of the most drought-tolerant shrub communities of the lower valleys was substantially reduced following the arrival of H. L. Shantz in 1908. Shantz, working with several other ecologists, undertook a study of the vegetation and soils of, first, Tooele Valley (Kearney et al. 1914) and then Escalante Valley (Shantz and Piemeisel 1940) that represented the first detailed ecological work conducted in the Basin. Shantz ranged over western Utah taking photographs—often to the frustration of his colleagues!—wherever he went. Because of his interest in agricultural capabilities of the land and the indicator value of this capability by natural vegetation, most of the Shantz photographs include lower valley areas, at least in the foreground of the scene. Shantz was also interested in vegetation change, and many of his photographs and notes refer to ecological successions taking place following disturbances such as plowing and burning.

Later photographs often match the scenes of earlier ones. R. R. Woolley, for example, matched photographs by Jackson and Gilbert during the 1930's and 1940's. In 1937 aerial photographs of parts of the Bonneville Basin became available. Intermediate photographs provide a valuable check on the progress of change and help prevent misinterpretations of the direction or rate of change that otherwise might result from unknown disturbances between the time of the original and match photographs.

Field Methods

Methods for matching old photographs are described by Harrison (1974) and Malde (1973). With the old photograph in hand, a search for the exact camera station is made in a trial and error process of repeated moves of the camera until the scene best matches the original. This can be very time consuming, especially when there are no identifiable foreground objects in the old and new scenes. Harrison describes a method that should be effective in such cases, but occasionally an accurate match can be obtained only after processing and printing the new negative, comparing the new print with the old, then returning to the site for a new match. Use of Polaroid films that produce both a positive and a negative shortly after exposure (R.P.S.P. 1979) reduces the problem but does not assure success because of the difficulty of comparing the usually smaller Polaroid

print with the field copy of the original. Detailed documentation of the camera station location, film and exposure information, and ecological observations should be prepared for each new photo while at the site (Fig. 11).

The level of detail that can be reached using photographic comparisons depends on several factors. If measurements are to be made on the photos, camera position, alignment, lens size, and other factors become crucial. For ecological work, however, such detail is generally not required. Photogrammetric information was not used in this study. Instead, qualitative assessments of increases or decreases in dominant species between the dates of the original and recent photos were used along with occasional estimates of cover and counts of individuals of particular species. In some cases measurements of growth rates would be useful, and then the methods described by Malde (1973) should be used. In this study detailed measurements would be difficult because of the lack of information about the old photographs and because of problems with identifying individual species in the original scenes. Future matches should be able to take advantage of the matches made in this study to increase the detail possible for each scene.

The value of most of the information called for in Fig. 11 is obvious, but a few items require further comment. The time of day (item 6) is usually unknown for the original photograph, and once the camera station is located it may be necessary to wait several hours, and sometimes until the next morning, to determine if shadow detail will match. If it does not, a return to the site at a later date may be necessary. Miscalculation of the date of the original could result in several return trips before a match could be made. In this study time of day was usually not considered. Possible misinterpretations arising from differences in shadows are discussed in the caption for each photograph pair as necessary. Only the photographs by Shantz were accompanied by dates. Misinterpretations that might arise from differences in season are included in the Comments (item 12) and are discussed when necessary in captions for the photographs.

Other important comments (item 12) include factors such as air quality, which will affect the apparent accuracy of the match, and other information that will assist in interpreting changes in the two photographs. Special observations relating to the objectives of the research may also be included in the comments. For this study previous land use, includ-

Repeat Photography Field Data

1. Number _____ 2. Photographer _____ 3. Date _____

4. Original photographer _____ 5. Original date _____

6. Time of day: Original _____ Match _____

7. Source of original _____ 8. Intermediate photos _____

9. Camera and film information:

    a. Roll/frame_____ _____ _____ _____ _____ _____ _____ _____

    b. Facing _____ _____ _____ _____ _____ _____ _____ _____

    c. Height _____ _____ _____ _____ _____ _____ _____ _____

    d. Dip angle _____ _____ _____ _____ _____ _____ _____ _____

    e. Strike _____ _____ _____ _____ _____ _____ _____ _____

    f. Lens _____ _____ _____ _____ _____ _____ _____ _____

    g. View angle ____ _____ _____ _____ _____ _____ _____ _____

    h. Aperture _____ _____ _____ _____ _____ _____ _____ _____

    i. Focus _____ _____ _____ _____ _____ _____ _____ _____

    j. Exposure _____ _____ _____ _____ _____ _____ _____ _____

    k. Film _____ _____ _____ _____ _____ _____ _____ _____

    l. Filter _____ _____ _____ _____ _____ _____ _____ _____

10. Location: Latitude _____ Longitude _____ Legal _____

    Altitude _____ General description _____

    _____

    _____

11. Vegetation: _____

    _____

    _____

    _____

    _____

    _____

    _____

12. Comments: _____

    _____

    _____

    _____

    _____

Fig. 11. Field data form.

ing qualitative estimates of past grazing and fire occurrence made from presence of dung and charcoal in the scene and near the camera station, were recorded.

The location (item 10) of the camera station should be described in general terms and marked in some way so as to simplify later matches. Harrison (1974) recommends that a steel rod be centered directly beneath the camera, and Turner used aluminum angles about 30 cm (12 in) long during his 1968–69 work in the Bonneville Basin. From 1976 to 1980, 41 of the matches by Turner were revisited and rephotographed. Only seven aluminum stakes were found in place. At three sites stakes were found lying near the camera station. Stakes may or may not have been placed at about a third of Turner's sites because of the presence of streets and other human developments. At one site a rock cairn had been built because the camera station was situated on a bedrock outcrop. The cause of the high attrition rate of Turner's stakes is uncertain, but livestock trampling, plowing, and other disturbances, coupled with my inability to locate the stake, are probably all responsible. Use of a steel rod would probably be more effective than the aluminum angle used by Turner because of the smaller above-ground surface area of the rod and because of the decreased visibility of a rusting steel surface. Decreased exposure would reduce disturbance but might result in loss of a greater proportion of stakes that could not be relocated even though they remained in place. Several of Turner's stakes were relocated by literally tripping over them while attempting to line up a match rather than while searching for the stake. Obviously, placing a small stake at the camera station is not an entirely satisfactory method of permanently marking the location. Monumenting the camera station using a heavy steel bar and a cement collar is probably the most certain solution to the problem but may be considered too costly and time consuming for most studies and would often be unfeasible in developed areas. Natural markers such as large rocks or trees are useful to witness the location, but these are often not present or will prove to be impermanent in the face of human activity. Perhaps the most effective and least expensive means for marking the camera station is a set of auxiliary photographs taken in a complete circle from the camera station, and a photograph of the camera tripod or other marker in place on the station. Microtopographic variation, as well as parallax information from several sources, greatly facilitates relocation of the exact camera station. Shantz frequently made multiple exposures from single locations, and accurate matches of such scenes are not difficult. Auxiliary photographs supplement the matched photographs and can provide valuable information in the future. In my study such photographs are assigned sequential numbers preceded by the letter "N," and are filed with the original and match photographs to which they are related.

Darkroom Techniques

Developing and enlarging match photographs follows standard procedures except that processing of film and paper for permanent storage is desirable. This is easily accomplished by using fiber-based papers and thoroughly fixing and washing film and prints. If enlargements from small negatives are to be made, fine-grain film should be used to preserve detail in the prints. Thirty-five mm Panatomic X film manufactured by Kodak was used for most of the matches made in this study. Enlargements of the new negatives, assuming the match was accurately located and centered on the old photograph, are conveniently made by placing the old photograph in the enlarging easel and focusing the new image on it before making the print. Technical references used throughout this study include the books by Blaker (1976), Sussman (1973), and the various technical manuals and instruction sheets provided by Eastman Kodak, Inc., and Polaroid, Inc.

The Plates

Matched photographs are grouped in four sections: (1) lower valleys, (2) upper valleys and foothills with sagebrush and grass, (3) upper valleys and foothills with juniper, and (4) upper valleys and foothills with oak and maple. Field observations are summarized in captions provided for each photo pair. Camera station locations include legal descriptions whenever maps containing this information were available. Estimates of annual rainfall, annual PE, and annual number of days without freezing temperatures are also included. Remarks in the captions referring to objects in the photographs make use of the locational terms given in Fig. 12.

Upper left Left background	Upper center Center background	Upper right Right background
Left center Left midground	Center Center midground	Right center Right midground
Lower left Left foreground	Lower center Center foreground	Lower right Right foreground

Fig. 12. Locational terms used to indicate objects in the photographs.

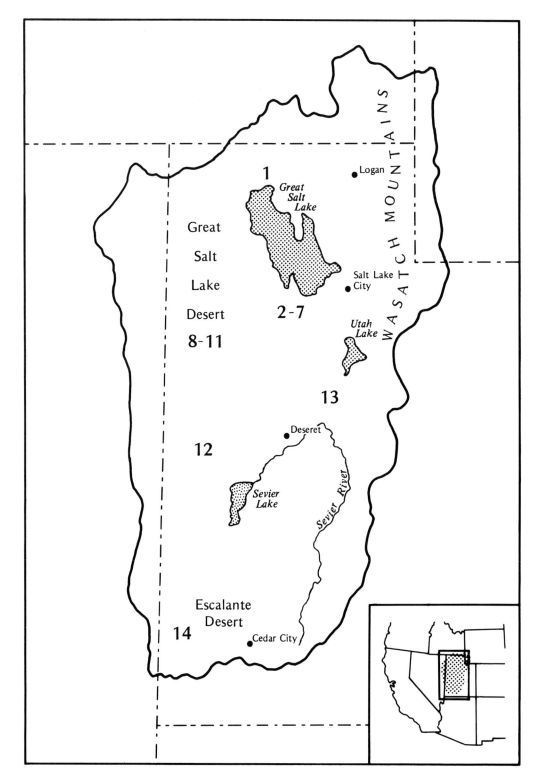

Fig. 13. Distribution of lower-valley matches.

LOWER VALLEYS

Fourteen matches illustrating changes in the shadscale zone are included in this section. Their general distribution in the study region is given in Fig. 13.

Plate 1. Great Salt Lake from Monument Point.
Location: The view is south from the SE¼ sec. 3, T. 11 N., R. 9 W., altitude 1317 m (4320 ft), at the north end of the lake.
Original: May 7, 8, or 9, 1869, Hart (left); Golden Spike National Historic Site. (Alfred Hart of Sacramento, California, was official photographer of the Union Pacific Railroad Company.)
Match: September 14, 1978, Rogers No. 424 (right).
Description: The shrub vegetation, now dominated by greasewood, shadscale, and iodine bush, within a matrix of cheatgrass and halogeton, has thickened somewhat, and a saltgrass meadow has developed on the near edge of the mud flats at left center. Saltgrass is serving as the pioneer plant following lake level decline. According to a

chart prepared by the U.S. Geological Survey (1977), water level in the lake was approximately 1284 m (4211 ft) in 1869, and increased to the historical maximum level of near 1284 m (4212 ft) in 1873. By 1905 the level had declined to 1279 m (4196 ft). Although fluctuations have been considerable up to the present, they have not exceeded 1282 m (4205 ft), which was reached in 1924. The 1924 level probably did not cover the area occupied by saltgrass, and thus it is likely that saltgrass could have spread onto the mud flat soon after 1873 and remained continuously to the present. Other species may have preceded saltgrass but none now occur along the lakeward margin of the meadow.

Climate: (averages for 1931–1960): Annual precipitation 23 cm (9 in), annual PE 65 cm (25.5 in), annual freeze-free season 170 days.

Plate 2. Tooele Valley.

Location: The view is southeast from within Tooele Army Depot. The camera station is about one-third of the distance from bunker M-1110 to bunker M-1109, about 10 m (33 ft) south of the connecting road. The camera station is in the N½ sec. 25, T. 3 S., R. 5 W., altitude 1420 m (4655 ft).

Original: August 3, 1912, Shantz No. P-7-12 (left).

Match: June 16, 1978, Rogers No. 404 (right).

Description: Shantz took two photos from this point enabling relocation with an error of no more than a few meters. The almost pure stand of green molly summercypress present in 1912 has been completely replaced by

several species of annuals, some shrubs, and some perennial grasses. Former bare areas are carpeted by bur buttercup, scattered cheatgrass, pepperweed (*Lepidium perfoliatum* L.), and other ephemeral herbs common to lower valley sites. The annuals were mature at the time of the match. The tall grass in the center of the match is sand dropseed; western wheatgrass (*Agropyron smithii* Rydb.) is common. Sagebrush, scattered along a line across the upper portion of the match, is spreading into the foreground. Livestock grazing is intensive, and the mature sagebrush plants have been severely damaged by trampling.

Climate: Annual precipitation 31 cm (12 in), annual PE 74 cm (29 in), freeze-free season 160 days.

Plate 3. South Mountain, south end of Tooele Valley.
Location. The view is southeast from the SE¼ sec. 3, T. 4 S., R. 5 W., just inside the south boundary of Tooele Army Depot, altitude 1624 m (4950 ft).
Original: June 3, 1912, Shantz No. d-1-12 (left).
Match: June 12, 1978, Rogers No. 113 (right).
Description: Annual vegetation dominated by cheatgrass has replaced the former shrubland dominated by green molly summercypress in the foreground and sagebrush on the slopes in the background. Other than an occasional individual snakeweed, the only shrubs in the scene are a few rubber rabbitbrush plants along the

shallow gullies in the upper center of the scene and some sagebrush on the slopes of South Mountain. Juniper occurring on the steeper slopes did not change much in abundance, but the pattern of its distribution has changed, possibly because it was cut for fuel or fence posts, but more likely due to fire. As with Plate 2, this site is grazed by sheep and is reported by Depot security personnel to be burned occasionally. As in several other shrubland scenes, ant discs are common in the original photograph but are not visible in the match. Whether this is due to a decline in the ant population or whether the current discs are simply hidden by annuals is uncertain.

Climate: Annual precipitation 31 cm (12 in), annual PE 70 cm (27.5 in), freeze-free season 150 days.

Plate 4. Grantsville, Tooele Valley.
Location: The view is north from the NW¼ sec. 15, T. 3 S., R. 5 W., about 5 km (3 mi) southeast of Grantsville. The camera station is just inside the fence along the north boundary of the Tooele Army Depot, altitude 1372 m (4501 ft).
Original: July 26, 1911, Shantz No. T-2-11 (left).
Match: October 5, 1978, Rogers No. 448 (right).
Description: The almost pure stand of shadscale present in 1911 has been replaced by annuals. Halogeton

dominates the foreground, bur buttercup dominates the right center of the scene, and cheatgrass with scattered mustards and Russian thistle occurs in dense stands along the floor of the wash in the upper center and upper left. Shrubs are present only on barren clay deposits on which few annuals occur. Shrub species present include winterfat, rubber rabbitbrush, shadscale, and others in small quantities. Bunchgrasses were found only in the shrub patches. Cheatgrass did not occur with shadscale, but winterfat was found growing in dense cheatgrass patches. The entire distribution could be the result of fire.

Climate: Annual precipitation 28 cm (11 in), annual PE 69 cm (27 in), freeze-free season 165 days.

Plate 5. East of Grantsville.
Location: The view is northwest from a small hill located in the NE¼ sec. 21, T. 2 S., R. 6 W. The Stansbury Mountains are at left.
Original: August 6, 1912, Shantz No. R-2-12 (left).
Match: October 2, 1978, Rogers No. 433 (right).
Description: Dominant shrubs of the fore- and midground include horsebrush, shadscale, sagebrush, and

snakeweed. Several other species are also present in varying quantities. The increase in size and number of the shrubs and grasses in the foreground is representative of a similar increase throughout the scene. Fire scars are common among the shrubs (a large one is present in the upper right near the base of the hills) and among the juniper on the hill slopes. With the exception of fire scars, juniper has increased in most areas on the slopes. *Climate:* Annual precipitation 31 cm (12 in), annual PE 64 cm (25 in), freeze-free season 165 days.

Plate 6. Timpie Valley, north end of the Stansbury Mountains.
Location: The camera station is across the road from power pole number 1922, about 17.7 km (11 mi) northwest of Grantsville, near the north end of the Stansbury Mountains. The view is south from the S½ sec. 23, T. 1 S., R. 7 W., altitude 1385 m (4220 ft).
Original: 1901(?), Gilbert No. 1838 (left).
Match: October 2, 1978, Rogers No. 131 (right).

Description: The greasewood shrub vegetation across the road may have thickened somewhat, but appears much the same in both pictures. The lighter band beyond the greasewood is dominated by cheatgrass and other annuals, as are the lighter patches at left center and center above the area of sagebrush that extends up the slopes beyond. Snakeweed is common throughout the sagebrush, especially where grazing has been heavy enough to result in trampling damage to sagebrush plants.

Climate: Annual precipitation 31 cm (12 in), annual PE 65 cm (25.5 in), freeze-free season 165 days.

Plate 7. Cedar Mountains from the west.
Location: The view is north from the S½ sec. 7, T. 4 S., R. 10 W., altitude 1719 m (5240 ft).
Original: 1901, Gilbert No. 1841 (left).
Match: September 1, 1976, Rogers No. 201 (right).

Description: The original shadscale vegetation has been replaced by cheatgrass and halogeton (dark plants) in the foreground and at some locations near the base of the mountains. Juniper has increased slightly on the slopes and has begun to spread onto the plain, particularly at left center.

Climate: Annual precipitation 28 cm (11 in), annual PE 64 cm (25 in), freeze-free season 150 days.

Plate 8. West base of Dugway Range.
Location: The camera is facing east from a point about 8 km (5 mi) northwest of Dugway Pass, Sec. 21 or 22, T. 10 S., R. 12 W., altitude 1575 m (4800 ft).
Original: 1901, Gilbert No. 1873 (left).
Match: September 13, 1976, Rogers No. 195 (right).

Description: The original vegetation dominated by horsebrush, Mormon tea, and shadscale appears little changed. Some of the original shrubs are still present, as are many of the juniper trees on the slopes. One tree (right center) died between photographs. At the time of the match, cheatgrass was abundant on the slopes and at their base. Snakeweed and halogeton were common.

Climate: Annual precipitation 20 cm (8 in), annual PE 74 cm (29 in), freeze-free season 150 days.

Plate 9. East face of the Fish Springs Range.
Location: The camera is facing south from a point about .4 km (.25 mi) west of Cain Spring, SE¼ T. 12 S., R. 14 W. The altitude of the camera is about 1372 m (4500 ft).
Original: 1901, Gilbert No. 1916a (left).
Match: September 15, 1976, Rogers No. 177a (right).

Description: Very little change is evident in the scene. Shadscale and horsebrush vegetation of the fore- and midground appears much the same in both photographs. Juniper has increased slightly on the Lake Bonneville beaches in the left center. Additional species common at the time of the match include snakeweed, Mormon tea, halogeton, and green molly summercypress.

Climate: Annual precipitation 20 cm (8 in), annual PE 79 cm (31 in), freeze-free season 155 days.

Plate 10. Lavender Buttes.
Location: The view is north from the S½, NW¼, T. 13 S., R. 15 W., altitude 1657 m (5050 ft), and shows the southernmost of a small group of rhyolite buttes just west of the middle part of the Fish Springs Range.
Original: 1901, Gilbert No. 1890 (left).
Match: May 14, 1978, Rogers No. 162 (right).
Description: The new photograph was taken a few meters farther back than the original. Consequently, when enlarged to match the original the foreground of the match is slightly more distant resulting in the foreground

shrubs appearing smaller. This effect may also be a partial result of a small increase in camera height for the match. Changes in the scene have not been very pronounced. Shrub species still dominate the foreground, and juniper appears about the same on the slopes of the butte. Common shrubs include horsebrush, shadscale, Mormon tea, black sagebrush, and a small Asteraceae that was not identified. Several bunchgrasses are present and appear to constitute a definite increase over the amount present in 1901. Galleta and Indian ricegrass were common.

Climate: Annual precipitation 20 cm (8 in), annual PE 71 cm (28 in), freeze-free season 160 days.

Plate 11. Lavender Buttes.
Location: The view is north from a saddle on the southwest side of the Buttes, about 2 km (1.2 mi) east of the Sand Pass road, NW¼ T. 13 S., R. 15 W. The altitude of the camera is about 1703 m (5190 ft). This site is located on the Granite Mountain Quadrangle on which the Buttes are named "Honeycombs."
Original: 1901, Gilbert No. 1906 (left).

Match: May 13, 1978, Rogers No. 166 (right).

Description: A few juniper have been added to the scene, and the growth of those present in the original scene is quite apparent. Small shrubs, including shadscale, horsebrush, Mormon tea, and black sagebrush, still dominate the scene but bunchgrasses (those in the foreground are galleta) have increased noticeably.

Climate: Annual precipitation 20 cm (8 in), annual PE 71 cm (28 in), freeze-free season 160 days.

Plate 12. Antelope Mountain, west face of the House Range.
Location: The camera station is about 5 km (3 mi) north of Rainbow Valley, 100 m (328 ft) west of the dirt road running north from the Valley. An aluminum stake left by R. M. Turner in 1968 is present at the camera station, altitude about 1372 m (4500 ft).
Original: 1901(?), Gilbert No. 1934a (left).
Match: July 14, 1979, Rogers No. 325 (right).
Description: The greasewood- (darker shrubs) and shadscale-dominated vegetation in the foreground has

changed very little during the 78-year period between photographs. Halogeton is now common near the camera station, and the lighter areas, particularly visible on the lower portion of the alluvial fan beyond the automobile, contain an abundance of halogeton and cheatgrass. The number of juniper trees on the steeper slopes has increased only moderately. The appearance of the increase is enhanced somewhat because of the higher contrast of the new photograph. Other matches throughout the House Range show the spread of cheatgrass and other annuals and the slight increase in juniper numbers illustrated by this match.

Climate: Annual precipitation 20 cm (8 in), annual PE 69 cm (27 in), freeze-free season 170 days.

Plate 13. High Mountains, north end of the Canyon Range.

Location: The view is east from the SW¼ sec. 33, T. 13 S., R. 4 W, between the highway and railroad, altitude 1512 m (4960 ft). The mountain range is named Gilson Mountains on some maps.

Original: August 30, 1913, Shantz No. LL-11-13 (top left).

Intermediate: August 3, 1969, Turner No. 655 (bottom left).

Match: May 13, 1978, Rogers No. 337 (right).

Description: Indian ricegrass, more abundant in the intermediate match, shares dominance with winter annuals in the 1978 photograph, perhaps because of the earlier date of the match. Winterfat, dominant in 1913, has become quite rare. A moderate increase of juniper occurring on the mountain slopes and onto the fan at the base of the mountain is apparent.

Climate: Annual precipitation 25 cm (10 in), annual PE 65 cm (25.5 in), freeze-free season 140 days.

Plate 14. Lund, Utah.

Location: The view is northwest from a point 5 km (3 mi) southwest of Lund. The camera station is about 175 m (577 ft) from the fence along the west side of the railroad, and is in the SE¼ sec. 36, T. 32 S., R. 15 W., altitude 1565 m (5130 ft).

Original: August 28, 1913, Shantz No. II-6-13 (left).

Match: September 9, 1977, Rogers No. 290 (right).

Description: According to the field notes made by Shantz, the small plants in the foreground of the original were saltbush, identified by Shantz as *Atriplex Nuttallii*, and the larger shrubs in the midground were fourwing

saltbush [*A. canescens* (Pursh) Nutt.]. According to Shantz the narrow lighter band beyond the fourwing saltbush was winterfat. Rubber rabbitbrush dominated beyond that, and sagebrush was present on the hills. By the time of Turner's 1968 match, the foreground had been taken over by halogeton. In 1977 halogeton still dominated the foreground and the rest of the scene remained much as described by Shantz except that juniper had increased on the lower hillslopes, especially in the upper right. Some patches of cheatgrass may have appeared at the base of the hills. In 1977 a few small saltbush plants were present in the foreground, probably the same species that dominated there in 1913.

Climate: Annual precipitation 23 cm (9 in), annual PE 64 cm (25 in), freeze-free season 115 days.

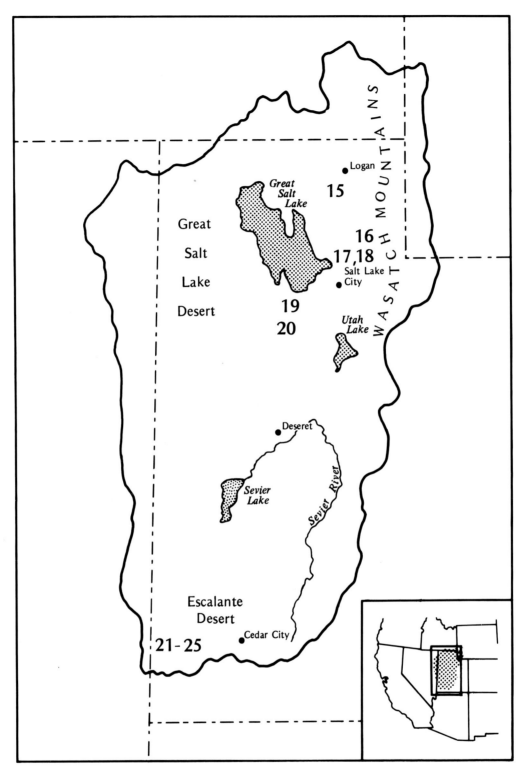

Fig. 14. Distribution of matches in upper valleys and foothills with sagebrush and grass.

UPPER VALLEYS AND FOOTHILLS
WITH SAGEBRUSH AND GRASS

Eleven matches illustrating changes in the upper valley sagebrush zone are included in this section. Their general distribution in the study region is given in Fig. 14.

Plate 15. Madsen, Utah.
Location: The view is southwest from a point east of Madsen. The camera station is in the NW¼ sec. 28, T. 11 N.,
R. 2 W., altitude 1356 m (4450 ft).
Original: 1901(?), Gilbert No. 3483 (top left).
Intermediate: July 20, 1968, Turner No. 500 (bottom left).
Match: September 3, 1978, Rogers No. 282 (right).
Description: Annuals appear to dominate much of the original scene and the match. Sagebrush dominates the
intermediate scene. Apparently a fire removed a stand of sagebrush prior to 1901, sagebrush became reestab-
lished by 1968, and another fire occurred between 1968 and 1978. Cheatgrass dominates the scene today. The
patch of trees at left is bigtooth maple.
Climate: Annual precipitation 46 cm (18 in), annual PE 69 cm (27 in), freeze-free season 150 days.

Plate 16. Witch's Rocks, Weber Canyon.
Location: The camera faces north from a point 2.5 km (1.5 mi) west of Echo, Utah, altitude 1719 m (5640 ft).
Original: 1869(?), O'Sullivan (left).
Match: July 18, 1978, Dingus (right).
Description: Much of the sagebrush present in 1869 has been replaced by cheatgrass and rubber rabbitbrush.

Some perennial grass may have been present in 1869, but little was present in 1978. Erosion of the conglomerate outcrops from which Witch's Rocks is formed is quite apparent. One column at left center has fallen, and the decrease in size of the others is obvious. The diameter of the column in the center of the photograph has been reduced to about one-half its 1869 size.

Climate: Annual precipitation 41 cm (16 in), annual PE 50 cm (19.5 in), freeze-free season 110 days.

Plate 17. Salt Lake City from the base of Ensign Peak.
Location: The camera faces southeast across a small unpaved road that runs north from the junction of the last paved city street and the dirt road that crosses City Creek Spur. Camera station altitude is 1670 m (5090 ft).
Original: 1868(?), O'Sullivan (left).
Match: March 15, 1980, Rogers No. 232 (right).
Description: Sagebrush, perhaps mixed with some grass, dominated the foreground in 1868. Few shrubs were

present in 1980. Snakeweed, cheatgrass, storksbill, and other annuals, mixed with Sandberg bluegrass and bluebunch wheatgrass, make up the foreground vegetation in the match. During the period 1976–80, six separate fires occurred on the foothills surrounding Salt Lake City. At least as many more may have occurred that I did not observe.

Climate: Annual precipitation 46 cm (18 in), annual PE 65 cm (25.5 in), freeze-free season 120 days.

Plate 18. Salt Lake City from the base of Ensign Peak.
Location: Same as Plate 17.
Original: Same as Plate 17 (left).
Match: March 15, 1980, Rogers No. 232a (right).

Description: This scene is from the same camera station as Plate 17 but with the camera turned more to the south. The change from shrub to grass and annual dominance is much the same as in Plate 17.
Climate: Same as Plate 17.

Plate 19. Tooele Valley.
Location: The view is north from near the reservoir (across the road to the left of the scene) on the Tooele Army Depot in the south end of the valley. The altitude is 1545 m (4710 ft) at the camera station, which is located near the center of sec. 25, T. 3 S., R. 5 W.
Original: August 3, 1912, Shantz No. O-9-12 (left).
Match: May 21, 1978, Rogers No. 369 (right).
Description: Shantz took 10 photographs in a complete circle enabling an exact relocation of the camera station.

Sagebrush, which dominated the scene in 1912, has been replaced by several species of annuals. Cheatgrass and storksbill are most abundant, but numerous other species are present, including sand dropseed, Sandburg bluegrass, red three-awn (*Aristida purpurea* Nutt.), and Indian ricegrass. Snakeweed is also common, as are moss and lichens. Sheep graze this area, and according to Tooele Army Depot security personnel, fires are common.

Climate: Annual precipitation 31 cm (12 in), annual PE 74 cm (29 in), freeze-free season 160 days.

Plate 20. South Mountain, Tooele Valley.
Location: The camera station is east of a small hill inside the southern boundary of the Tooele Army Depot. The view is southwest from the SW¼ sec. 3, T. 4 S., R. 5 W., at altitude 1611 m (4910 ft).
Original: June 13, 1912, Shantz No. D-5-12 (left).
Match: June 12, 1978, Rogers No. 115 (right).
Description: Apart from the small patch of green molly summercypress, the original scene is dominated by

sagebrush and stands of juniper below the beaches and on the slopes of South Mountain. The foreground of the match, which is today heavily disturbed by vehicular traffic, is dominated by pepperweed and lesser amounts of cheatgrass, crested wheat grass [*Agropyron cristatum* (L). Gaertn.], storksbill, snakeweed, and bur buttercup. The remainder of the scene, up to the base of South Mountain, is dominated by cheatgrass. The juniper stands on the mountain slopes have thickened and expanded, but the stand below the beach has almost disappeared. *Climate:* Annual precipitation 31 cm (12 in), annual PE 70 cm (27.5 in), freeze-free season 150 days.

Plate 21. Escalante Desert.
Location: The camera faces northwest from a point north of the railroad near the second switching bunker and butane tanks northeast of Modena. This camera station is about 9 km (5.5 mi) northeast of Plates 22 and 23, altitude about 1608 m (5276 ft).
Original: August 27, 1913, Shantz No. HH-6-13 (left).
Match: September 5, 1977, Rogers No. 288 (right).
Description: This scene, also matched by Turner in 1968, shows very little change in the overall quantities of the

two dominant species—galleta and little rabbitbrush. Within the fenced railroad right-of-way other species are common. As noted by Turner, these include Indian ricegrass, winterfat, and several species of grass not evident in the scene outside the right-of-way. Livestock grazing is heavy, and probably influences the variation among species present. A detailed investigation of the galleta/little rabbitbrush vegetation was not conducted to determine whether or not the species present inside the ungrazed right-of-way were present but smaller in size due to grazing in the area outside.

Climate: Annual precipitation 20 cm (8 in), annual PE 62 cm (24.5 in), freeze-free season 130 days.

Plate 22. Two miles northeast of Modena.
Location: The view is west from a point west of the railroad, about .8 km (.6 mi) northeast along the railroad from the semaphore switching boxes. The camera station is about 6 m (20 ft) west of the right-of-way fence, and its altitude is approximately 1788 m (5450 ft).
Original: August 27, 1913, Shantz No. HH-1-13 (left).
Match: October 21, 1968, Turner No. 514x (right).

Description: The death of sagebrush evident in the original photo was attributed by Shantz to greater competitive ability of galleta grass. This explanation may be incomplete, however, because of the increase of sagebrush that occurred by 1968, despite the continued presence of galleta. Numerous sagebrush seedlings are visible throughout the 1968 scene, indicating that complete domination of the foreground may occur eventually. Plate 23 shows the continued sagebrush expansion between 1968 and 1977.

Climate: Annual precipitation 23 cm (9 in), annual PE 62 cm (24.5 in), freeze-free season 130 days.

Plate 23. Expansion of sagebrush in galleta.
Location: Same as Plate 22.
Original: October 21, 1968, Turner No. 514x (left).
Match: September 5, 1977, Rogers No. 286 (right).
Description: The increase of sagebrush during the nine-year period between photographs is obvious. Sagebrush

seedlings are common, indicating that the expansion is continuing. The ability of galleta to replace sagebrush or prevent its spread through competition appears quite small since sagebrush seedlings are present in even the densest stands of galleta. The dead sagebrush plants in the 1913 scene (Plate 22) could have been killed by a variety of factors, such as drought, disease, and fire, other than competition with galleta.

Climate: Same as Plate 22.

Plate 24. East of Modena.
Location: The view is northwest from a point .7 km (.4 mi) north of Antelope Drive, and 43 m (141 ft) west of Fifth Street, in an uninhabited subdivision on the north side of State Highway 56, 5 km (3 mi) east of Modena, altitude about 1638 m (5374 ft).
Original: September 13, 1915, Shantz No. QQ-1-15 (left).
Match: September 5, 1977, Rogers No. 287 (right).

Description: As in Plate 22, Shantz attributed the death of sagebrush to competition with galleta. A match by Turner made in 1968 and the recent match again show the ready invasion of galleta by sagebrush. Sagebrush seedlings, though not as apparent as in Plates 22 and 23, are abundant in this scene as well.

Climate: Annual precipitation 20 cm (8 in), annual PE 64 cm (25 in), freeze-free season 120 days.

Plate 25. Antelope Peak, Escalante Desert.
Location: The view is south from the center of sec. 33, T. 34 S., R. 14 W. The camera station is about 1 m (3 ft) from the east side of a sheep corral and about 10 m (33 ft) from the northeast corner of the corral, altitude 1726 m (5261 ft).
Original: September 8, 1914, Shantz No. Y-3-14 (left).
Match: September 4, 1977, Rogers No. 296 (right).
Description: According to Shantz's notes, the dominant grasses in the foreground of the original are three-awn

and galleta, and the principal shrub is saltbush, probably fourwing saltbush. According to Turner's field notes made at the time of his 1968 match, three-awn was abundant on the low ridge in the upper left of the scene and galleta was still common. Fourwing saltbush was rare, and Russian thistle and cheatgrass were abundant. Rubber rabbitbrush was the dominant shrub in the scene in 1968, as it was in 1977. Russian thistle, which dominated the heavily trampled foreground of the scene in Turner's match, had been replaced by Belvedere summercypress by 1977.

Climate: Annual precipitation 20 cm (8 in), annual PE 55 cm (21.5 in), freeze-free season 130 days.

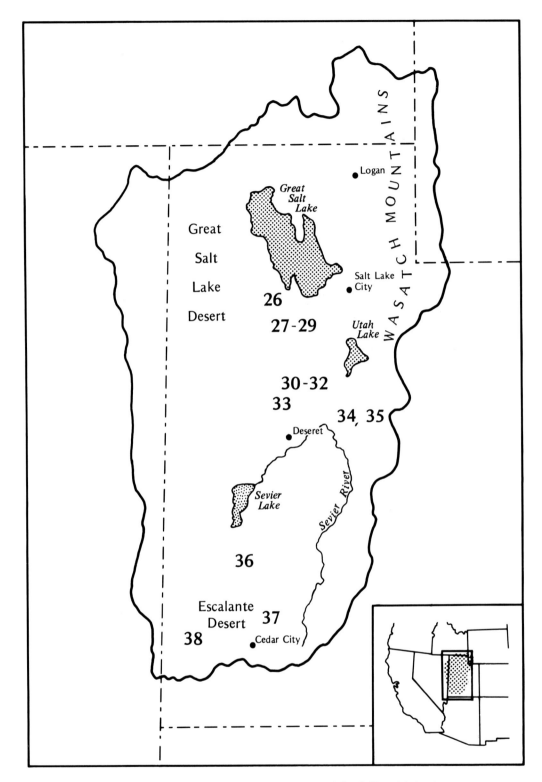

Fig. 15. Distribution of matches in upper valleys and foothills with juniper.

UPPER VALLEYS AND FOOTHILLS
WITH JUNIPER

Thirteen matches illustrating changes involving sagebrush and juniper are included in this section. Their general distribution in the study region is given in Fig. 15.

Plate 26. North end of the Cedar Mountains.
Location: The camera station is atop the north end of the Cedar Mountains at approximately 2034 m (6200 ft). The view is south.
Original: September 26, 1916, Shantz No. II-3-16 (left).
Match: August 31, 1976, Rogers No. 154 (right).
Description: Very little change has taken place. Bluebunch wheatgrass, horsebrush, black sagebrush, and juniper, the species listed by Shantz, are present in about the same proportions in both photographs. Other species present include snakeweed, winterfat, and a small Asteraceae shrub. Most features of the scene,

including rocks in the foreground and a juniper branch in the lower center, have remained undisturbed during the 60 years between photos suggesting that disturbance by grazing or fire has been minimal. The rate of growth of individual juniper trees has been very slow. At similar elevations on the west slope of the Stansbury Mountains (Plates 27-29) tree growth has been much more rapid, probably because of greater orographic precipitation induced by the larger mass and greater elevation of the Stansbury Range. Most of the apparent differences in the position of the small stones in the foreground is a result of different sun angle. Shantz photographed the scene in the morning and my match was made in the afternoon.

Climate: Annual precipitation 20 cm (8 in), annual PE 69 cm (27 in), freeze-free season 160 days.

Plate 27. West slope of the Stansbury Mountains.
Location: The camera faces north from the NE¼ sec. 12, T. 4 S., R. 8 W., near the mouth of Big Creek Canyon, altitude 1743 m (5720 ft).
Original: 1901, Gilbert No. 1849 (left).
Match: April 19, 1980, Rogers No. 129 (right).
Description: Numerous juniper stumps in the original suggest that fire may have removed a former juniper woodland similar to that present in 1980. The former woodland may have been less dense, however, because the

density of stumps is less than the 1980 tree density. By 1901 sufficient time had elapsed since the earlier fire for sagebrush to dominate the site but much of the sagebrush has been replaced by juniper. A recent fire burned across the camera station leaving behind vegetation dominated by cheatgrass, bluebunch wheatgrass, and other herbs. The replacement of sagebrush by juniper since 1901 is typical of western slopes of the Stansbury Mountains.

Climate: Annual precipitation 38 cm (15 in), annual PE 55 cm (21.5 in), freeze-free season 150 days.

Plate 28. Stansbury Mountains.

Location: The view is northeast from the S½ sec. 13, T. 4 S., R. 8 W., altitude 1657 m (5050 ft). The mountains are to the right. Salt Mountain is visible in the right center of the scene.

Original: 1901, Gilbert No. 1843 (left).

Match: September 2, 1976, Rogers No. 124 (right).

Description: Juniper is replacing the sagebrush community that dominated the original scene. The new camera station is on top of a large rock about 30 m (97 ft) farther back (south) than the original. The small clearing in the

foreground is not typical, but this position was selected for the match to enable viewing the Lake Bonneville shore spits in the distance. From the original camera position most of the scene was blocked by juniper in the foreground. Herbaceous vegetation has increased not only in the clearing but at the original position as well. Sandburg bluegrass is dominant and is common throughout the woodland. Small amounts of cheatgrass, snakeweed, and cactus (*Opuntia* Mill.) are also present.

Climate: Annual precipitation 36 cm (14 in), annual PE 57 cm (22.5 in), freeze-free season 170 days.

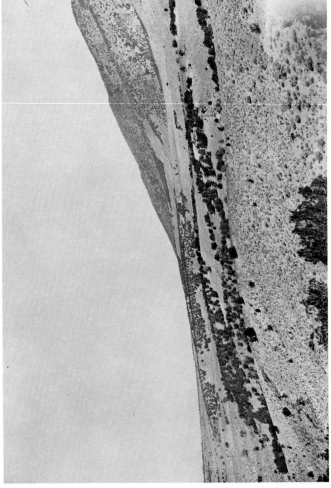

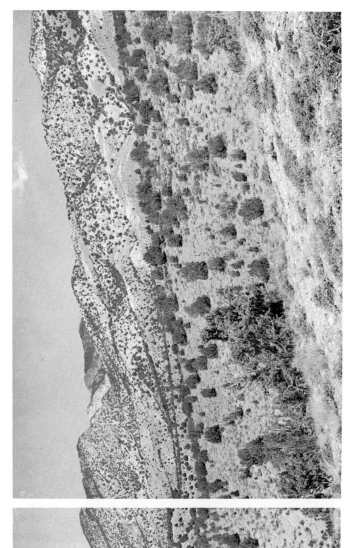

Plate 29. Stansbury Mountains.

Location: This site is 4.8 km (3 mi) east of the Skull Valley Indian Reservation near the road to Dry Canyon. The camera is stationed on a large lob of the piedmont just inside the Wasatch National Forest boundary about 200 m (644 ft) north of the road. The view is north from the NW¼ sec. 8, T. 5 S., R. 7 W., altitude 1936 m (5900 ft).

Original: 1901, Gilbert Nos. 1850, 1850a (left).

Match: September 3, 1976, Rogers Nos. 130, 130a (right).

Description: Identities of dominant species have not changed, but relative abundance of the species has. Juniper has increased in all areas, and young trees and seedlings are abundant. The increase has been greatest in the areas of low slope angle at the left and least on the mountain slopes at right. Trees present in 1901 are easily identified, and a number of stumps and snags visible in the earlier photographs are still present. The right foreground is dominated by black sagebrush with some hymenoxys [*Hymenoxys acaulis* (Pursh) Parker] and Sandburg bluegrass. These species are abundant in the understory throughout the maturing woodland, but big sagebrush replaces black sagebrush to the left. Herbs are common, but only one small patch of cheatgrass was found near the camera station.

Climate: Annual precipitation 41 cm (16 in), annual PE 56 cm (22 in), freeze-free season 140 days.

Plate 30. Point Lookout from north of Lookout Pass.
Location: The view is south from a hill overlooking the old Pony Express route, T. 8 S., R. 6 W., altitude 1951 m (6400 ft).
Original: 1901, Gilbert No. 1855 (left).
Match: April 27, 1980, Rogers No. 140 (right).

Description: Foreground shrubs of the original have been replaced by cheatgrass and snakeweed. Evidence of fire is common near the camera station. The slopes of Point Lookout are dominated by sagebrush and juniper, and a considerable increase of juniper has taken place and is continuing.

Climate: Annual precipitation 41 cm (16 in), annual PE 61 cm (24 in), freeze-free season 115 days.

Plate 31. North face of Red Pine Mountain.

Location: This camera station is on a slope above a corral, about 5 km (3 mi) south of the Pony Express route. It is reached by a dirt road that turns south about 1.6 km (1 mi) west of Lookout Pass. The view is southeast, altitude 2231 m (6800 ft).

Original: 1901, Gilbert No. 1857 (left).

Match: April 26, 1980, Rogers No. 142 (right).

Description: On the mountain slopes pinyon has increased, as has Douglas fir [*Pseudotsuga menziesii* (Mirb.) Franco] in the steep canyons. Increases on lower slopes have been made by juniper and several shrub species

including serviceberry [*Amelanchier alnifolia* (Nutt.) Nutt.], cliffrose [*Cowania mexicana* D. Don var. *stans-buriana* (Torr.) Jeps], curlleaf mountain mahogany (*Cercocarpus ledifolius* Nutt.), and squawbush (*Rhus trilobata* Nutt. in T. & G.). Sagebrush is common throughout the scene, and cheatgrass and snakeweed are abundant on the lower slopes and the sloping plain at the left. Grasses appear to have increased on the plain, and those present include Sandburg bluegrass, bluebunch wheatgrass, and Indian ricegrass. Most of the increase in the foreground has been by juniper and cliffrose. Large patches of bark had been removed from most pinyon on the slopes, perhaps by porcupines.

Climate: Annual precipitation 41 cm (16 in), annual PE 53 cm (21 in), freeze-free season 100 days.

Plate 32. North face of Red Pine Mountain.
Location: Same as Plate 31, but the view here is south.
Original: 1901, Gilbert No. 1857a (left).
Match: April 26, 1980, Rogers No. 142a (right).
Description: The description given for Plate 31 applies to this scene as well. In addition, it can be seen that the

many small light patches that were probably ant discs present on the ridge and slope running across the middle of the scene have all disappeared. The juniper tree in the foreground appears to have grown from the small juvenile present in the original.

Climate: Same as Plate 31.

Plate 33. West base of Simpson Range.
Location: The camera station is on a large gravel bar about 150 m (482 ft) west of the road that runs along the west side of the mountains. The view is northeast from the N½ sec. 30, T. 10 S., R. 8 W., altitude 1709 m (5210 ft).
Original: 1901, Gilbert No. 1861 (left).
Match: September 12, 1976, Rogers No. 133 (right).
Description: The foreground community has changed very little. Horsebrush is dominant, but other species,

including big sagebrush, Mormon tea, shadscale, snakeweed, black sagebrush, and cactus, are abundant. Grasses, including Sandburg bluegrass, bluebunch wheatgrass, Indian ricegrass, and cheatgrass, have increased since 1901. Large areas across the center of the scene that were formerly occupied by shrubs are now dominated by cheatgrass. Juniper has increased, especially on the pediments and alluvial fans, but also on steeper mountain slopes.

Climate: Annual precipitation 41 cm (16 in), annual PE 65 cm (25.5 in), freeze-free season 130 days.

Plate 34. Sand Mountain, west of High Mountain.
Location: The view is west from a small hill on the east side of State Highway 50, in the SE½ sec. 33, T. 13 S., R. 4 W., altitude 1585 m (5200 ft). The camera station of Plate 13 is near the left center edge of the scene.
Original: August 30, 1913, Shantz No. LL-12-13 (left).
Match: May 13, 1978, Rogers No. 338 (right).

Description: Shadscale, dominant in the foreground of the original scene, has decreased somewhat, and snakeweed and cheatgrass have increased. Juniper has decreased probably because of fire. Charred stumps are numerous beyond the railroad near the sand-dune field.

Climate: Annual precipitation 23 cm (9 in), annual PE 65 cm (25.5 in), freeze-free season 140 days.

Plate 35. San Pitch Mountains south of Nephi.
Location: The camera is facing east from a point about 6.4 km (4 mi) south of Nephi, SE¼ sec. 30, T. 13 S., R. 1 E., altitude 1616 m (5300 ft).
Original: July 29, 1910, Shantz No. L-4-10 (left).

Match: July 4, 1979, Rogers No. 300 (right).
Description: Juniper has increased substantially on the foothills while Gambel oak (upper right center) remained much the same, but with some increase in size of clones.
Climate: Annual precipitation 38 cm (15 in), annual PE 64 cm (25 in), freeze-free season 140 days.

Plate 36. West slope of the Mineral Mountains.
Location: The view is west from sec. 19, T. 28 S., R. 9 W., altitude 1737 m (5700 ft). The town of Milford is visible on the valley floor in the distance.
Original: September 9, 1913, Shantz No. QQ-7-13 (left).
Match: October 25, 1968, Turner No. 519x (right).
Description: Few changes have taken place in this scene. The match I made in 1977 is almost identical to that by

Turner shown here. A few juniper present in the original (left center) have disappeared, and several young juniper have appeared in the match. Fire may be responsible for removal of the trees missing from the original (some charred stumps were found near the camera station), but wood cutting may have occurred as well. Fire has not occurred recently, however, as indicated by the vigorous stand of sagebrush extending from the foreground downslope through the scattered juniper.

Climate: Annual precipitation 23 cm (9 in), annual PE 53 cm (21 in), freeze-free season 110 days.

Plate 37. Parowan, Utah.
Location: The camera faces southeast from the NW¼ T. 34 S., R. 8 W., altitude about 1830 m (6000 ft).
Original: September 6, 1914, Shantz No. V-8-14 (left).
Match: July 4, 1979, Rogers No. 317 (right).
Description: The foreground sagebrush community has been removed for agricultural purposes and the juniper

on the slopes has increased. Sometime before 1968 when this scene was matched by Turner the alluvial fan at left center had been cleared, probably by chaining. In 1979 reoccupation of the cleared area by juniper was well underway.

Climate: Annual precipitation 36 cm (14 in), annual PE 61 cm (24 in), freeze-free season 105 days.

Plate 38. Enterprise, Utah.
Location: The view is west from within T. 37 S., R. 17 W., altitude 1829 m (6000 ft).
Original: September 9, 1914, Shantz No. Y-7-14 (left).
Match: October 19, 1968, Turner No. 508a (right).

Description: Disturbances in the foreground and along the road running through the center of the scene have resulted in sagebrush replacement by annuals and snakeweed. Juniper is increasing in sagebrush throughout the scene.

Climate: Annual precipitation 31 cm (12 in), annual PE 62 cm (24.5 in), freeze-free season 140 days.

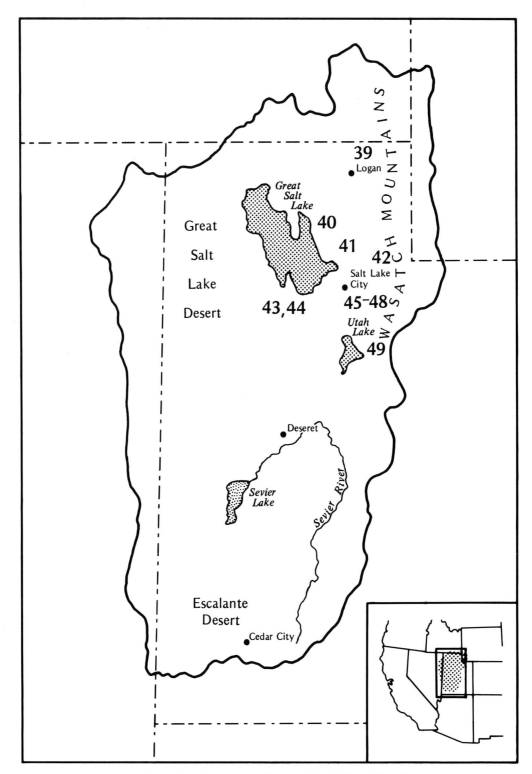

Fig. 16. Distribution of matches in upper valleys and foothills with oak.

UPPER VALLEYS AND FOOTHILLS
WITH OAK

Eleven matches illustrating changes in oak and maple vegetation are included in this section. General distribution of the matches in the study region is given in Fig. 16.

Plate 39. Dry Canyon, Logan, Utah.

Location: The view is south from a delta overlooking the mouth of Dry Canyon. The camera station is in the SE¼ sec. 35, T. 12 N., R. 1 E., altitude 1524 m (5000 ft).

Original: 1901(?), Gilbert No. 3414, published as Plate 1-A in U.S. Geological Survey Professional Paper 153, 1928 (left).

Match: September 28, 1977, Rogers No. 280 (right).

Description: Bigtooth maple has increased on the slopes and at left center. No oak is present. Juniper has also increased, particularly in the upper left of the scene, and numerous seedlings are present on the slope. Most of the grass that dominated the foreground and valley floor in 1901 has been replaced by annuals, especially cheatgrass.

Climate: Annual precipitation 51 cm (20 in), annual PE 72 cm (28.5 in), freeze-free season 160 days.

Plate 40. Wasatch Mountains from Willard Bay State Park.
Location: The camera faces east across a parking lot near a boat ramp in the SW¼ sec. 22, T. 8 N., R. 2 W., altitude 1280 m (4200 ft).
Original: 1901(?), Gilbert No. 3417b (left).
Match: September 28, 1977, Rogers No. 278 (right).

Description: Oak clones have increased somewhat in size throughout the scene and numerous new clones are present, particularly at right center. Juniper has increased at several places on the slopes. The largest stand of juniper is near the center of the scene beyond the transmission tower. In several instances juniper has grown up in oak clones.

Climate: Annual precipitation 43 cm (17 in), annual PE 70 cm (27.5 in), freeze-free season 150 days.

Plate 41. North of Ogden Canyon mouth.
Location: The camera faces north from the NE¼ sec. 22, T. 6 N., R. 1 W., altitude 1420 M (4660 ft).
Original: 1901(?), Gilbert No. 3480 (left).
Match: June 20, 1980, Rogers No. 274 (right).
Description: This is a highly disturbed site and probably has been since long before 1901 because of its proximity to Ogden, Utah, one of the earliest settlements of the region. Unidentified grasses dominated the site in 1901, along with scattered prickly pear [*Opuntia fragilis* (Nutt.) Haw.] and a few juniper in the upper right. The few shrubs present are restricted to the fault scarps in the center and left center of the scene. In 1968 when the scene

was matched by Turner shrubs were abundant but were still concentrated on the scarps. Most of the original juniper were gone and several new ones had appeared. Two oak clones had appeared (indicated by arrows in the 1980 match), and a cottonwood tree (*Populus* L.) was growing at left center. By 1980 fire had apparently swept most of the scene removing many of the shrubs present in 1968. Rubber rabbitbrush remained much the same along the road and in the left foreground, and the new juniper and oak were still present and had increased in size. Grass was common in 1980, but cheatgrass and other annuals dominated the vegetation.

Climate: Annual precipitation 51 cm (20 in), annual PE 65 cm (25.5 in), freeze-free season 150 days.

Plate 42. Sentinel Rock, Echo Canyon.
Location: This site is about 1.6 km (1 mi) northeast of Echo, Utah, altitude 1734 m (5690 ft).
Original: 1869, Jackson No. 30 (left).
Match: October 1, 1977, Rogers no. 209 (right).
Description: Oak and maple are present in the match in about the same proportion as in 1869, but the number of juniper has increased. Sagebrush, which was originally abundant, has been replaced over much of the scene by

cheatgrass. The original photograph and others of Sentinel Rock by Jackson and O'Sullivan were matched about 1940 by Woolley and again in 1968 by Turner. The site had burned prior to the 1940 match, and numerous charred stumps were present in the vicinity of the camera station in 1977. Perennial bunchgrass appears to be more abundant in this and other matches than it was in 1869.

Climate: Annual precipitation 41 cm (16 in), annual PE 50 cm (19.5 in), freeze-free season 100 days.

Plate 43. Tooele, Utah.
Location: This hillside is just south of Tooele on the east side of State Highway 36. The view is southeast from the SE¼ sec. 32, T. 3 S., R. 4 W., altitude 1763 m (5100 ft).
Original: June 8, 1912, Shantz No. E-3-12 (left).
Match: August 20, 1976, Rogers No. 116 (right).
Description: The foreground of this scene is highly disturbed although it is no longer used for agriculture as it

was in 1912. Much of the shrub-dominated vegetation across the road has been replaced by annuals, chiefly cheatgrass. On the slope sagebrush has increased somewhat, and the talus garlands, composed of bigtooth maple, chokecherry [*Prunus virginiana* L., possibly var. *melanocarpa* (A. Nels.) Sarg.], and squawbush, have expanded. Only one small oak was found in 1976. It is near the top of the hill in the upper right and was not visible in 1912.

Climate: Annual precipitation 41 cm (16 in), annual PE 70 cm (27.5 in), freeze-free season 155 days.

Plate 44. Tooele, Utah.
Location: The view is east from atop One O'Clock Hill overlooking Tooele. The hilltop is in the SW¼ sec. 33, T. 3 S., R. 4 W., altitude 1779 m (5835 ft).
Original: August 3, 1912, Shantz No. q-3-12 (left).
Match: October 5, 1978, Rogers No. 450 (right).
Description: Cheatgrass has replaced the sagebrush that dominated the hilltop in 1912. Bluebunch wheatgrass,

visible in the lower right of the original scene, is still present along with some Sandburg bluegrass. Snakeweed and sagebrush seedlings are abundant. Evidence of recent fire in the form of charred sagebrush is widespread on this and neighboring hills. Gambel oak has increased in number and size on the slopes across the valley and on the mountainsides in the background.

Climate: Annual precipitation 43 cm (17 in), annual PE 69 cm (27 in), freeze-free season 150 days.

Plate 45. Wasatch Mountains near Little Cottonwood Canyon.
Location: The camera is facing northeast from the SE¼ sec. 2, T. 3 S., R. 1 E., altitude 1564 m (5130 ft).
Original: 1901, Gilbert No. 1823a (left).
Match: September 13, 1977, Rogers No. 263 (right).
Description: The sagebrush present in the oak growing in the foreground has diminished somewhat. Oak clones

on the slopes across the center of the scene have increased in size and many small new clones have appeared. A fire recently burned the slope in the right half of the middle section of the photograph, but the clones present, including many small new ones, are recovering rapidly.

Climate: Annual precipitation 56 cm (22 in), annual PE 64 cm (25 in), freeze-free season 165 days.

Plate 46. Wasatch Mountains north of Little Cottonwood Canyon.
Location: The camera is facing east from the same position as Plate 45.
Original: 1901, Gilbert 1823b (left).
Match: September 13, 1977, Rogers No. 264 (right).
Description: This photograph was taken from the same camera station as Plate 45 and further illustrates the

increase of oak on the slopes of the mountains. Maple has also increased, and the many new trees growing in the shallow ravines at right center and upper right are distinguishable from the oak in which they are growing by their lighter tones. The maples are not restricted to ravines, however, and have appeared in oak clones throughout the scene.

Climate: Same as Plate 45.

Plate 47. Little Cottonwood Canyon.
Location: The camera faces east into the mouth of the Canyon from the SW¼ sec. 7, T. 3 S., R. 2 E., altitude 1646 m (5400 ft).
Original: 1901, Gilbert No. 1817 (top left).
Intermediate: July 13, 1968, Turner No. 472 (bottom left).
Match: September 19, 1977, Rogers No. 267 (right).
Description: Oak clones have increased in size and number, and bigtooth maple has appeared in the oak clones above the sagebrush-covered slope at right center and has spread onto the slope. A considerable increase in size and number of maples has taken place since 1968. Most of the new trees on the slope in the right center of the scene are maple, but a few scattered oak are present as well. According to a local resident, the slope was grazed until about 1967. Counts of annual growth rings of two large sagebrush on the slope yielded mean ages of 30 and 35 years.
Climate: Annual precipitation 64 cm (25 in), annual PE 55 cm (23 in), freeze-free season 110 days.

Plate 48. Corner Canyon, Salt Lake Valley.
Location: The view is southwest across Corner Creek from the NW¼ sec. 3, T. 4 S., R. 1 E., altitude 1588 m (5210 ft).
Original: 1901, Gilbert No. 1828 (left)
Match: June 26, 1978, Rogers No. 259 (right).
Description: Oak clones on the Traverse Mountains in the left center and center of the scene have increased in size and number. Clones have also increased on the Lake Bonneville beach extending across the scene to the base of the Traverse Mountains. Decline of sagebrush as clones thicken is evident in the large patches of oak at right center. Similar increases of **oak and** decreases of sagebrush are apparent in the foreground of Plates 45 and

46. Oak clones on the creek bank just beyond the trees in the foreground are in the early stages of recovery from a recent fire. The area burned is outlined and identified with the letter A. An earlier fire burned across area B just west of area A, and may have included part or all of A. Area A was dominated by cheatgrass and other annuals in 1978, but numerous sagebrush seedlings were present. Area B was dominated by young sagebrush plants and annuals. The rapid reinvasion by sagebrush indicates that without additional fires, both areas will probably be completely reoccupied by sagebrush in a decade or two. All oaks damaged by the fires appear to be recovering rapidly.

Climate: Annual precipitation 51 cm (20 in), annual PE 69 cm (27 in), freeze-free season 129 days.

Plate 49. Bridal Veil Falls.
Location: The view is south across Provo Canyon about 40 m (131 ft) east of Lost Creek. The camera station is in the SE¼ sec. 33, T. 5 S., R. 3 E., altitude 1706 m (5200 ft).
Original: 1869(?), O'Sullivan No. 28 (left).
Match: September 12, 1977, Rogers No. 339 (right).

Description: Vegetation throughout the scene has thickened considerably. Oak dominates the foreground, but several other shrub species are present, including curlleaf mountain mahogany, bigtooth maple, and boxelder (*Acer negundo* L.).

Climate: Annual precipitation 71 cm (28 in), annual PE 53 cm (21 in), freeze-free season 90 days.

Results

From all the matched photographs three general trends emerge. The first is the increasing prevalence of weedy annuals in all habitats. The second is the general increase in quantity of vegetation. The third is the greater stability (persistence) of communities dominated by species that resprout after being damaged.

Lower Valleys

Photographs of vegetation on the saline valley floors are too few to provide much insight into changes occurring there. Saltgrass was found to be capable of colonizing exposed salt flats following lake decline (Plate 1), but the rate at which this occurs cannot be determined from the photographs alone. Greasewood appears to have remained about the same, but with some increase in size and number of plants (Plates 1, 6, 12). Green molly summercypress was replaced by annuals and perennial grasses at two locations (Plates 2 and 3). Annuals increased on formerly bare ground (Plates 2 and 14) and were abundant at all locations.

Vegetation dominated by shadscale was replaced by annuals at two locations (Plates 4 and 7), but changed little in other scenes. Horsebrush communities tended to be stable but appear somewhat thicker. Winterfat disappeared at one location (Plate 13).

Fires have apparently been common in the shadscale zone in recent years. No other mechanism accounting for complete removal of shrubs and replacement by annual vegetation is as likely as fire in the areas depicted by the photographs. Removal by livestock grazing is unlikely because of low palatability of several species, including the dominant—shadscale. Removal for agricultural purposes is also unlikely because of poor soils and low rainfall and because many sites are too rocky or steep for cultivation.

Upper Valleys and Foothills with Sagebrush and Grass

Sagebrush vegetation is common in upper valleys and foothills dominated by both juniper (Plates 26-38) and oak (Plates 39-49) and with few exceptions has undergone obvious changes. Generally it has given way before the expansion of other species. In the north the change has been toward dominance by annuals (Plates 15-20), but in the south sagebrush has increased in galleta-dominated grasslands (Plates 21-24). At three locations former sagebrush stands, indicated by dead plants in the original photographs, have redeveloped (Plates 15, 22-24), and at one site a former sagebrush stand reappeared and was then replaced by annuals (Plate 15).

As with shadscale, removal or reduction of former sagebrush stands may be a result of fire. Other causes such as drought and consumption by insects or rodents are also possible, and from the photographic evidence alone the actual cause cannot be determined. Charcoal was found on plant remains at only two sites (Plates 15 and 30).

Upper Valleys and Foothills with Juniper

Juniper trees have increased mainly at the expense of sagebrush in nearly all locations. The increase was very slow at two sites (Plates 26 and 36) and at one location (Plate 34) juniper declined. Juniper is visible in photographs included in the preceeding and following sections, and changes there have been similar to those apparent in the matches included in this section. In the Sheeprock Mountains (Plates 31 and 32), expansion by other species, including pinyon, serviceberry, and cliffrose, has been extensive. Charcoal was found on juniper stumps at the sites shown in Plates 26, 27, 29, 34, and 36.

At some locations where juniper has expanded into

sagebrush there are no stumps visible in the original photograph (e.g., Plates 30-32, 38). At other sites stumps are much more scattered in the original photograph than are the trees in the match (Plates 27-29). Although stumps left when fire destroyed an earlier woodland might have been cut for fuel or fence posts, it seems more likely that sites without stumps were not occupied by a former woodland, at least not for several hundred years. Juniper decays very slowly, and tree remains visible in early photographs often appear almost unchanged in the matches (e.g., Plate 26).

Upper Valleys and Foothills with Oak

Oak clones have increased in size and number almost universally in the study area, including all photograph pairs from the Wasatch Mountains and two pairs from the west side of the Oquirrh Mountains (Plates 43 and 44). The expansion, particularly in number of clones, probably occurred mainly after 1900. Intermediate match photographs and aerial photographs from the 1930's and 1940's show that numbers of clones increased rapidly after 1940, particularly at sites in Salt Lake Valley. Maple has increased in a similar fashion (e.g., Plate 39), and numerous saplings have appeared in recent years, particularly on north-facing slopes (Plate 47). Evidence of recent fires was found at several locations (Plates 15, 42, 45, 48).

DISCUSSION OF RESULTS

Based on the published research record, and the evidence provided by the matched photographs, it is possible to construct some rather general theories regarding the changes that have occurred and to speculate about what the future course of events might be. Before beginning, however, I would like to stress that this discussion is an expression of opinion rather than fact. My justification for including the following speculations is the hope that they will contribute to the formation of plans for future research.

For vegetation dominated by perennial grass, sagebrush, and juniper, the theory goes like this: Shortly after settlement in the middle 1800's large numbers of domestic livestock were imported to the region creating much greater grazing pressure than formerly existed (Young et al. 1976). The changes associated with grazing may have arisen in three ways. *First,* grazing weakens the more palatable species, including perennial grasses and some shrub species, allowing increases to occur among less palatable shrubs, trees, and annual weeds. *Second,* grazing eliminates much of the herbaceous vegetation that would otherwise provide fine fuel to assist the spread of shrub and tree destroying fires, and combined with other factors such as road construction and fire control programs, has caused a reduction in fire frequency (Burkhardt and Tisdale 1976). *Third,* spread of highly competitive introduced annuals has contributed to the decline of native grasses while at the same time producing greater concentrations of fine fuel. As a result fire frequency has begun to increase to the point that perennial grasses and shrubs have no opportunity to become established and reach reproductive maturity (Young et al. 1971). These ideas are contained in Fig. 17.

The first and second sources of change produce vegetation dominated by woody shrubs and trees, and the third produces permanent weed communities. The photographic evidence could easily be taken to support these sources of change. The shrub communities present in some of the early 1900 photographs may represent the earlier replacement of grasses by shrubs, and the expansion of juniper may represent the gradual encroachment of the slower growing trees in the absence of fire. Replacement of former communities by annuals as a result of competition and fire could also easily be inferred from the photographs.

Change in lower valley communities might follow a similar path, but would probably be slower. Because plants are often widely spaced, fire would be less frequent, and because the palatable species are often shrubby, their reduction by grazing would not greatly affect the normal fire regime. Grazing alone may be insufficient to remove palatable shrubs (Norton 1978, Rice and Westoby 1978, West 1979a), but it may have facilitated the spread of annual weeds, leading to an increase in fire frequency, and creating conditions similar to the cycle projected by Fig. 17.

A major problem with this theory is that of proving that fire frequency declined after settlement. It is possible burning increased rather than decreased. Fire was used by early settlers to remove sagebrush (Pickford 1932), and although fires might have easily been ignited, controlling them would have been difficult. Access to many parts of the study area by surface vehicle is difficult today, and would have

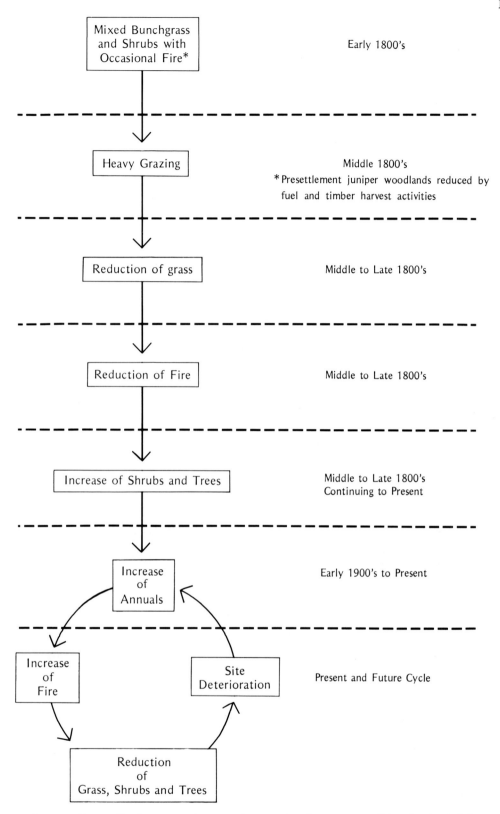

Fig. 17. Generalized post-settlement changes in plant communities dominated by perennial grass, sagebrush, and juniper. The sequence projected in this figure assumes that the presettlement vegetation consisted largely of mixed stands of sagebrush and grass maintained by occasional fire. Juniper woodlands that existed at the time of settlement may have been depleted at many locations to meet the need for fuel and timber (see Young and Budy 1979). The cyclic deterioration associated with annual weed increase and resultant fire-frequency increase is just beginning in many places. Whether or not annuals will eventually replace other species over most of the Desert remains to be seen.

been more so during the 1800's. Even with the modern fire-fighting equipment now available, one occasionally hears about a "prescription" fire that escaped control and burned a much larger area than planned. Although modern fire-fighting technology has become quite advanced, this technology was not in existence in the nineteenth century. For example, much of our current fire control ability is dependent on the use of fire retardant dropped from airplanes and helicopters. As described by Linkewich (1972), however, the use of airplanes in fire control is a relatively recent development. The first successful "bombing" of a fire was accomplished in Canada in 1950. Burkhardt and Tisdale (1976) suggest that roads, which act as firebreaks, are one way in which fire has been reduced by human intervention. The number of roads present in the 1800's was not great, however, and in many places in the Bonneville Basin today roads are few in upper valleys and foothills surrounding many of the Basin mountain ranges.

If it cannot be shown that settlement led to fire reduction because of fire prevention activity, what other explanations for reduced fire occurrence exist? One possibility that has been documented elsewhere (Aschmann 1977, and see articles in Stokes and Dieterich 1980) is that fires were frequently set by Indians, and that this activity was curtailed following settlement. Although it is known that Indians of western Utah used fire to drive game (Egan 1917), the extent to which this actually occurred in the Bonneville Basin remains conjectural (Cottam 1976). A second possibility, which is discussed below, is that the climate of the region has become more favorable for the growth of woody species making fire reduction less important in explaining the change.

The expansion of oak and maple during this century cannot be explained by fire and grazing alone. Because of their ability to resprout, these species tend to resist replacement by other species, and successions that begin with fire and move through a sequence of dominant species do not occur. In the following discussion I explore the possibility that climate change may have been involved in the increase of these species.

In photographs taken in 1868 and 1869 (e.g., Plate 49), oak clones were smaller, appeared less vigorous, and were fewer in number than in photographs taken after 1900. In 1901, clones were generally larger than in earlier photographs, but new clones were still infrequent. While individual clones continued to grow larger after 1901, the most pronounced change during this century has been the increase in number of small clones.

Christensen (1949) hypothesized that oak was expanding in response to shifting climate, but that the expansion was restricted by grazing. It is possible, however, that grazing could promote sprouting within older clones and could favor clone enlargement. These views are not entirely incompatible. According to Christensen, the expansion would primarily occur because of dispersal of acorns and because of establishment of new clones from the extended root systems of existing clones. Seedling establishment from acorns is rare (Christensen 1949), but sprouting from roots is common. In either case, young plants would probably be more susceptible to grazing damage than would mature clones.

Conceivably, increased grazing and man-caused fires during the late 1800's led to increased sprouting and growth of individual clones, but prevented appearance of new ones. Following establishment of national forests in Utah between 1897 and 1908, management plans were prepared, and numbers of livestock were reduced, particularly after 1930 (Roberts and Gardner 1964). Fire frequency probably declined as well. Along the eastern margin of the Wasatch Mountains the reduction in livestock numbers was probably greater than at many other locations. This was because of flooding in 1923 and 1930 that was thought to be a result of plant cover reduction by livestock grazing on watersheds in the mountains (Bailey 1941, Croft et al. 1943, DeByle and Hookano 1973). Reduced grazing and fire occurrence could have allowed new clones to become established.

Increased size of established clones as a result of grazing or man-caused fires does not explain the poor condition of clones photographed in 1869. Many of the 1869 photographs were taken near cities and towns where grazing and intentional burning were likely to have been heavy for as long as 22 years (Walker 1964). Oak resprouts rapidly after fire (Kunzler and Harper 1980), and thickening of clones following grazing would probably occur at least as quickly, well within 22 years. Other factors, such as disease, insect attack, or perhaps extremely heavy grazing might be involved. Drought should not have been a factor because the climate of the region was generally moist at mid-century (Wahl and Lawson 1970), and winter precipitation, of significance to oak development (Tew 1967), was high from 1866 to 1890, except for 1876 to 1880 (Bradley 1976). The factor of greatest importance may have been the more frequent extreme winter freezes and more common late spring frosts that may have occurred during and prior to the middle 1800's due to the prevalence of more southerly storm tracks during the period (Gribbin and Lamb 1978).

By combining grazing, fire, and climate, a simple theory explaining oak expansion might be stated like this: From the early to late 1800's, extreme winter cold and late spring frosts produced the poor condition of oak clones visible in the 1869 photographs. During the late 1800's temperatures became less extreme, enabling expansion by existing clones. Then, as described above, reduced grazing and fire in the early to middle 1900's allowed the increase in number of small new clones visible in recent photographs.

This theory is particularly weak because of the lack of information about the response of oak to freezing and grazing. The rate of response probably varies as the intensity of each factor varies, and the differential importance of the factors taken together is unknown. Even were this information known, the theory would be very difficult to prove. Weather station records are not available for the first half of the nineteenth century, and the dendroclimatological information currently available is not useful for climate reconstruction in the central Wasatch Mountains. Similarly, records of the intensity and duration of livestock grazing at particular locations are often unavailable. Because of these limitations, it is impossible to compose a supportable theory until further studies of oak response to grazing and climate are conducted.

Were it found that climate change had indeed favored oak expansion, it might be possible to use this information to help explain the rapid expansion of other woody species since 1901. As pointed out in the Results section, there appears to have been a general thickening of vegetation at many sites in the Bonneville Basin. Burkhardt and Tisdale (1976) and Blackburn and Tueller (1970) include climate as a potential factor in the increase of juniper, and Holmgren and Hutchings (1972) and Beatley (1980) cite climate as a factor in the changes occurring in the shadscale zone. If climate has become more favorable for the growth of woody species, this would diminish the importance of reduced fire frequency following settlement as an explanation for the spread of sagebrush and juniper. In the Sonoran Desert, Hastings and Turner (1965) concluded that the increase of woody species over a period similar to that considered in this study was at least partly due to climate

change. Although inclusion of climate as a factor in the changes would require an alteration of the sequence of events contained in Fig. 17, it would not alter the potential for environmental deterioration associated with the increase of introduced annuals projected by the figure.

CONCLUSION

My speculations concerning grazing, fire, and climate provide only tentative explanations for the changes. Not only are early records of important factors limited, but our understanding of vegetation response to them is very poor. The numbers of livestock, the specific places they grazed, and the annual duration of their grazing will probably never be known for most of the Great Basin Desert. Likewise, the frequency and extent of past fires is unknown, except for the past few years. Climate reconstructions that allow more than general speculation may never be achieved because of the shortage of climatic records from the early part of the 1800's. Studies of grazing effects on plants, and studies of past climate and fire occurrence recorded in tree rings, may eventually provide some explanations, but so many other factors remain to be considered (e.g., Young and Budy 1979) that complete solutions seem very unlikely. The importance of explaining the initial causes of the changes may have become eclipsed, however, by the need to deal with problems arising from the spread of introduced weeds.

Frequent appearance of annual-dominated vegetation in the new photographs may herald a new age in Great Basin natural history. As annuals become more prevalent, fire frequency will increase (West 1979b), productivity will decrease, and the likelihood of soil erosion will increase (Beatley 1966, Hulbert 1955, Hull and Hansen 1974, Sneva 1965, Young and Evans 1978). These, and other characteristics of environmental deterioration, have been widely discussed under the heading 'desertification' (Glantz 1977, United Nations Conference on Desertification 1977).

The transformation of native perennial vegetation to ephemeral herbs that grow during spring and early summer is probably encouraged by any activity that damages native vegetation. Sources of damage include excessive grazing, burning, and poorly planned management programs involving shrub and tree eradication. Fires that once might have been beneficial in providing vegetation patterns that included mixtures of grasses, shrubs, and trees may no longer be desirable. Unlike grazing and eradication, however, control of fire may be impossible. Records of man-caused fires occurring in Utah indicate little change in numbers of fires or acres burned, despite a ten-fold increase in funds spent in fire suppression and presuppression efforts during the past 20 years (U.S. Bureau of Land Management 1958-79, U.S. Forest Service 1960-79).

The problems associated with introduced annuals are quite familiar to today's ecologists and managers (e.g., Young et al. 1979), and efforts are being made to find the means to continue to use the land without allowing its deterioration. Despite the progress being made, many questions remain. As research continues, and management plans are revised, it seems that the accumulation of ecological knowledge, and its application, is always too little too late. Current plans for the Bonneville Basin include major power production facilities and military defense projects. Other activities may be expected to increase in relation to currently planned projects as well as probable future developments. Without increased attention to basic research and planning, the inescapable conclusion is that the introduced annuals that are adapted to frequent disturbance will continue to replace the more stable native vegetation, probably at an accelerating rate.

Appendix:
SOURCES OF ORIGINAL AND INTERMEDIATE PHOTOGRAPHS

Plate	Date Original	Match	Location	Original Photographer	No.	Source of Original
1	1869	1978	Monument Point	Hart		Golden Spike Natl. Historic Site
2	1912	1978	Tooele Valley	Shantz	P-7-12	Herbarium, Univ. of Arizona
3	1912	1978	South Mountain	Shantz	d-1-12	Herbarium, Univ. of Arizona
4	1911	1978	Grantsville	Shantz	T-2-11	Herbarium, Univ. of Arizona
5	1912	1978	Grantsville	Shantz	R-2-12	Herbarium, Univ. of Arizona
6	1901(?)	1978	Timpie Valley	Gilbert	1838	U. S. G. S. Photo Library
7	1901	1976	Cedar Mountains	Gilbert	1841	U. S. G. S. Photo Library
8	1901	1976	Dugway Range	Gilbert	1873	U. S. G. S. Photo Library
9	1901	1976	Fish Springs Range	Gilbert	1916a	U. S. G. S. Photo Library
10	1901	1978	Lavender Buttes	Gilbert	1890	U. S. G. S. Photo Library
11	1901	1978	Lavender Buttes	Gilbert	1906	U. S. G. S. Photo Library
12	1901(?)	1979	House Range	Gilbert	1934a	U. S. G. S. Photo Library
13	1913	1978	High Mountains	Shantz	LL-11-13	Herbarium, Univ. of Arizona
(intermediate)		1969		Turner	655	R. M. Turner, Botanist, U.S.G.S.
14	1913	1977	Lund	Shantz	II-6-13	Herbarium, Univ. of Arizona
15	1901	1978	Madsen	Gilbert	3483	U. S. G. S. Photo Library
(intermediate)		1968		Turner	500	R. M. Turner, Botanist, U.S.G.S.
16	1869		Witch's Rocks	O'Sullivan		U. S. G. S. Photo Library
(match)		1978		Dingus		R. Dingus, R. P. S. P.
17	1868(?)	1980	Salt Lake City	O'Sullivan		U. S. G. S. Photo Library
18	1868(?)	1980	Salt Lake City	O'Sullivan		U. S. G. S. Photo Library
19	1912	1978	Tooele Valley	Shantz	O-9-12	Herbarium, Univ. of Arizona
20	1912	1978	South Mountain	Shantz	D-5-12	Herbarium, Univ. of Arizona
21	1913	1977	Escalante Desert	Shantz	HH-6-13	Herbarium, Univ. of Arizona
22	1913		Modena	Shantz	HH-1-13	Herbarium, Univ. of Arizona
(match)		1968		Turner	514x	R. M. Turner, Botanist, U.S.G.S.
23	1968	1977	Modena	Turner	514x	R. M. Turner, Botanist, U.S.G.S.
24	1915	1977	Modena	Shantz	QQ-1-15	Herbarium, Univ. of Arizona
25	1914	1977	Escalante Desert	Shantz	Y-3-14	Herbarium, Univ. of Arizona
26	1916	1976	Cedar Mountains	Shantz	II-3-16	Herbarium, Univ. of Arizona
27	1901	1980	Stansbury Mountains	Gilbert	1849	U. S. G. S. Photo Library
28	1901	1976	Stansbury Mountains	Gilbert	1843	U. S. G. S. Photo Library
29	1901	1976	Stansbury Mountains	Gilbert	1850,1850a	U. S. G. S. Photo Library
30	1901	1980	Lookout Pass	Gilbert	1855	U. S. G. S. Photo Library
31	1901	1980	Red Pine Mountain	Gilbert	1857	U. S. G. S. Photo Library
32	1901	1980	Red Pine Mountain	Gilbert	1857a	U. S. G. S. Photo Library
33	1901	1976	Simpson Range	Gilbert	1861	U. S. G. S. Photo Library
34	1913	1978	Sand Mountain	Shantz	LL-12-13	Herbarium, Univ. of Arizona
35	1910	1979	San Pitch Mountains	Shantz	L-4-10	Herbarium, Univ. of Arizona
36	1913		Mineral Mountains	Shantz	QQ-7-13	Herbarium, Univ. of Arizona
(match)		1968		Turner	519x	R. M. Turner, Botanist, U.S.G.S.
37	1914	1979	Parowan	Shantz	V-8-14	Herbarium, Univ. of Arizona
38	1914		Enterprise	Shantz	Y-7-14	Herbarium, Univ. of Arizona
(match)		1968		Turner	508a	R. M. Turner, Botanist, U.S.G.S.
39	1901(?)	1977	Dry Canyon	Gilbert	3414	U. S. G. S. Photo Library
40	1901(?)	1977	Willard Bay	Gilbert	3417b	U. S. G. S. Photo Library
41	1901(?)	1980	Ogden Canyon	Gilbert	3480	U. S. G. S. Photo Library
42	1869	1978	Sentinel Rock	Jackson	30	U. S. G. S. Photo Library
43	1912	1976	Tooele	Shantz	E-3-12	Herbarium, Univ. of Arizona
44	1912	1978	Tooele	Shantz	q-3-12	Herbarium, Univ. of Arizona
45	1901	1977	Little Cottonwood Canyon	Gilbert	1823a	U. S. G. S. Photo Library
46	1901	1977	Little Cottonwood Canyon	Gilbert	1823b	U. S. G. S. Photo Library
47	1901	1977	Little Cottonwood Canyon	Gilbert	1817	U. S. G. S. Photo Library
(intermediate)		1968		Turner	472	R. M. Turner, Botanist, U.S.G.S.
48	1901	1978	Corner Canyon	Gilbert	1828	U. S. G. S. Photo Library
49	1869(?)	1977	Bridal Veil Falls	O'Sullivan	28	U. S. G. S. Photo Library

References

Aldon, Earl F., and H. W. Springfield. 1973. The southwestern pinyon-juniper ecosystem: a bibliography. U.S. Forest Service General Technical Report RM–4. 20 p.

Allman, Verl Phillips. 1953. A preliminary study of the vegetation in an exclosure in the chaparral of the Wasatch Mountains, Utah. Utah Academy of Sciences, Arts and Letters, Proceedings 30:63–73.

Anderson, Jay E., and Karl E. Holte. 1981. Vegetation development over 25 years without grazing on sagebrush-dominated rangeland in southeastern Idaho. Journal of Range Management 34:25–29.

Arnow, Lois A., and Ann M. Wyckoff. 1977. Flora of the Central Wasatch Front, Utah. University of Utah Printing Service, Salt Lake City, Utah. 459 p.

Aschmann, Homer. 1977. Aboriginal use of fire. U.S. Forest Service General Technical Report WO–3:132–141.

Bailey, Reed W. 1941. Land-erosion—normal and accelerated—in the semiarid West. American Geophysical Union, Transactions of 1941: 1–14.

Barney, Milo A., and Neil C. Frischknecht. 1974. Vegetation changes following fire in the pinyon-juniper type of west-central Utah. Journal of Range Management 27:91–96.

Beatley, Janice C. 1966. Ecological status of introduced brome grasses (*Bromus* spp.) in desert vegetation of southern Nevada. Ecology 47:548–554.

————. 1980. Fluctuations and stability in climax shrub and woodland vegetation of the Mojave, Great Basin and transition deserts of southern Nevada. Israel Journal of Botany 28:149–168.

Beeson, Dwight W. 1974. The distribution and synecology of Great Basin pinyon-juniper. Master's thesis. University of Nevada—Reno. 91 p.

Beetle, Alan A. 1979. Autecology of selected woody sagebrush species, p. 23–26. *In* The sagebrush ecosystem: a symposium. Utah State University, College of Natural Resources. 251 p.

Blackburn, Wilbert H., and Paul T. Tueller. 1970. Pinyon and juniper invasion in black sagebrush communities in east-central Nevada. Ecology 51:841–848.

Blaker, Alfred A. 1976. Field photography: beginning and advanced techniques. W. H. Freeman and Company, San Francisco. 451 p.

Bradley, Raymond S. 1976. Precipitation history of the Rocky Mountain States. Westview Press, Boulder, Colorado. 334 p.

Burkhardt, J. Wayne, and E. W. Tisdale. 1969. Nature and successional status of western juniper vegetation in Idaho. Journal of Range Management 22:264–270.

————, and E. W. Tisdale. 1976. Causes of juniper invasion in southwestern Idaho. Ecology 57:472–484.

Child, R. Dennis. 1970. Recovery of desert range plants in various states of vigor during a seven year period of non-use. Master's thesis. Utah State University. 87 p.

Christensen, Earl M. 1949. The ecology and geographic distribution of oak brush (*Quercus gambelii*) in Utah. Master's thesis. University of Utah. 90 p.

————. 1950. Distributional observations of oak brush (*Quercus gambelii* Nutt.) in Utah. Utah Academy of Sciences, Arts and Letters, Proceedings 27:22–25.

————. 1955. Ecological notes on the mountain brush in Utah. Utah Academy of Sciences, Arts and Letters, Proceedings 32:107–111.

————. 1957. Photographic history of the mountain brush on "Y" Mountain, central Utah. Utah Academy of Sciences, Arts and Letters, Proceedings 34:154–155.

————. 1958a. A comparative study of the climates of mountain brush, pinyon-juniper and sagebrush communities in Utah. Utah Academy of Sciences, Arts and Letters, Proceedings 6:174–175. (Abstr.)

————. 1958b. Growth rates and vegetation change in the oak-maple brush in lower Provo Canyon, Utah. Utah Academy of Sciences, Arts and Letters, Proceedings 35:167–168.

————. 1961. The deciduous tree communities of central Utah. Bulletin of the Ecological Society of America 42:62–63.

————. 1962. The root system of Bigtooth Maple. Great Basin Naturalist 22:114–115.

————. 1963. The foothill bunchgrass vegetation of central Utah. Ecology 44:156–158.

————. 1964a. Succession in a mountain brush community in central Utah. Utah Academy of Sciences, Arts and Letters, Proceedings 41:10–13.

————. 1964b. Changes in composition of a *Bromus tectorum-Sporobolus cryptandrus-Aristida longiseta* community following fire. Utah Academy of Sciences, Arts and Letters, Proceedings 41:53–57.

Cline, Gloria Griffen. 1963. Exploring the Great Basin. University of Oklahoma Press, Norman, Okla. 254 p.

Cook, C. Wayne. 1977. Effects of season and intensity of use on desert vegetation. Utah Agricultural Experiment Station Bulletin 483. 57 p.

Cottam, Walter Page. 1926. An ecological study of the flora of Utah Lake, Utah. Ph.D. dissertation. University of Chicago. 129 p.

143

————. 1929. Man as a biotic factor illustrated by recent floristic and physiographic changes at Mountain Meadows, Washington County, Utah. Ecology 10:361–363.

————. 1947. Is Utah Sahara bound? Bulletin of the University of Utah 37:1–40.

————. 1976. The impact of man on the flora of the Bonneville Basin. Department of Geography, University of Utah, Research Paper No. 76–1. 8 p.

————, and George Stewart. 1940. Plant succession as a result of grazing and meadow desiccation by erosion since settlement in 1862. Journal of Forestry 38:613–626.

————, J. M. Tucker, and R. Drobnick. 1959. Some clues to Great Basin postpluvial climates provided by oak distributions. Ecology 40:361–377.

Croft, A. R., Lowell Woodward, and Dean A. Anderson. 1943. Measurement of accelerated erosion on range-watershed land. Journal of Forestry 41:112–116.

Cronquist, Arthur, Arthur H. Holmgren, Noel H. Holmgren, and James L. Reveal. 1972. Intermountain flora: vascular plants of the intermountain west, U.S.A. Hafner Publishing Company, New York. 270 p.

Currie, Pat O. 1963. Food habits of the blacktailed jackrabbit (*Lepus californicus*), and forage competition between jackrabbits and domestic livestock on native range in northwestern Utah. Ph.D. dissertation. Utah State University. 81 p.

DeByle, Norbert V., and Ezra Hookano, Jr. 1973. Research related to the Davis County Experimental Watershed: an annotated bibliography. U.S. Forest Service General Technical Report INT–4. 16 p.

Durrant, Stephen D. 1952. Mammals of Utah, taxonomy and distribution. University of Kansas Publications, Museum of Natural History 6:1–549.

Eastmond, Robert J. 1968. Vegetational changes in a mountain brush community of Utah during eighteen years. Master's thesis. Brigham Young University. 67 p.

Egan, William M., ed. 1917. Pioneering the West, 1846–1878, Major Howard Egan's Diary. Howard R. Egan Estate, Richmond, Utah. 302 p.

Fautin, R. W. 1946. Biotic communities of the northern desert shrub biome in western Utah. Ecological Monographs 16:251–310.

Flowers, Seville. 1934. Vegetation of the Great Salt Lake region. Botanical Gazette 95:353–418.

Foster, Robert H. 1968. Distribution of the major plant communities in Utah. Ph.D. dissertation. Brigham Young University. 124 p. + map in pocket.

Frischknecht, Neil C. 1975. Native faunal relationships within the pinyon-juniper ecosystem, p. 55–65. *In* Proceedings of the Pinyon-Juniper Symposium, Utah State University, Logan, Utah.

————, and Maurice F. Baker. 1972. Voles can improve sagebrush rangelands. Journal of Range Management 25:466–468.

Gates, D. H., L. A. Stoddart, and C. W. Cook. 1956. Soil as a factor influencing plant distribution on salt deserts of Utah. Ecological Monographs 26:155–175.

Glantz, Michael H., ed. 1977. Desertification: environmental degradation in and around arid lands. Westview Press, Boulder, Colorado. 346 p.

Gleason, Henry A., and Arthur Cronquist. 1964. The natural geography of plants. Columbia University Press, New York. 420 p.

Gribbin, John, and H. H. Lamb. 1978. Climatic change in historical times, p. 68–82. *In* John Gribbin, ed., Climatic change. Cambridge University Press, Cambridge. 280 p.

Grime, J. P. 1979. Plant strategies and vegetation processes. Wiley-Interscience, Somerset, New Jersey. 222 p.

Gruell, George E. 1980. Fire's influence on wildlife habitat on the Bridger–Teton National Forest, Wyoming. Volume 1—Photographic record and analysis. U.S. Forest Service Research Paper INT–235. 207 p.

Harper, Kimball T. 1959. Vegetational changes in a shadscale-winterfat plant association during twenty-three years of controlled grazing. Master's thesis. Brigham Young University. 64 p.

————, and James L. Reveal, Symposium Organizers. 1978. Intermountain biogeography: a symposium. Great Basin Naturalist Memoirs 2:1–268.

Harrison, A. E. 1974. Reoccupying unmarked camera stations for geological observations. Geology 2:469–471.

Hastings, James Rodney, and Raymond M. Turner. 1965. The changing mile. University of Arizona Press, Tucson. 317 p.

Hayward, C. Lynn. 1948. Biotic communities of the Wasatch chaparral, Utah. Ecological Monographs 18:473–506.

Holmgren, Ralph C. 1975. The Desert Experimental Range: description, history, and program, p. 18–22. *In* D. N. Hyder, ed., Arid Shrublands—proceedings of the third workshop of the United States/Australia Rangelands Panel, Tucson, Arizona. 148 p.

————, and Selar S. Hutchings. 1972. Salt desert shrub response to grazing use, p. 152–164. *In* McKell, Cyrus M., James P. Blaisdell, and Joe R. Goodin, eds., Wildland shrubs—their biology and utilization. U.S. Forest Service General Technical Report INT–1. 494 p.

————, and James L. Reveal. 1966. Checklist of the vascular plants of the intermountain region. U.S. Forest Service Research Paper INT–32. 160 p.

Hulbert, Lloyd C. 1955. Ecological studies of *Bromus tectorum* and other annual bromegrasses. Ecological Monographs 25:181–213.

Hull, A. C., Jr., and W. Theron Hansen, Jr. 1974. Delayed germination of cheatgrass seed. Journal of Range Management 27:366–368.

————, and Mary Kay Hull. 1974. Presettlement vegetation of Cache Valley Utah and Idaho. Journal of Range Management 27:27–29.

Hunt, Charles B. 1974. Natural regions of the United States and Canada. W. H. Freeman and Company, San Francisco. 725 p.

Hutchings, Selar S. and George Stewart. 1953. Increasing forage yields and sheep production on Intermountain winter ranges. U.S.D.A. Circular No. 925. 63 p.

Jeppson, Roland W., Gaylen L. Ashcroft, A. Leon Huber, Gaylord V. Skogerboe, and Jay M. Bagley. 1968. Hydrologic atlas of Utah. Utah Water Research Laboratory,

Utah Agricultural Experiment Station, Utah State University, and Division of Water Resources, Utah Department of Natural Resources. PRWG 35–1. 306 p.

John, Rodney T., and Norman I. Bowden, Project Leaders. 1974. Big game harvest report. Utah State Division of Wildlife Resources, Publication No. 75–2. 94 p.

Kearney, T. H., L. J. Briggs, H. L. Shantz, J. W. McLane, and R. L. Piemeisel. 1914. Indicator significance of vegetation in Tooele Valley, Utah. Journal of Agricultural Research 1:370–417.

Kuchler, A. W. 1964. Potential natural vegetation of the conterminous United States. American Geographical Society, New York. Special Publication No. 36.

Kunzler, L. M. and K. T. Harper, 1980. Recovery of Gambel oak after fire in central Utah. Great Basin Naturalist 40:127–130.

Linkewich, Alexander. 1972. Air attack on forest fires, history and techniques. D. W. Fiesen and Sons, Calgary, Alberta. 321 p.

Malde, H. E. 1973. Geologic bench marks by terrestrial photography. U.S. Geological Survey Journal of Research 1:193–206.

Martin, P. S. 1967. Prehistoric overkill. In P. S. Martin and H. E. Wright, Jr., eds., Pleistocene extinctions, the search for a cause. Yale University Press, New Haven. 453 p.

Mather, John R., and Gary A. Yoshioka. 1966. The role of climate in the distribution of vegetation, p. 372–384. In Douglas B. Carter and John R. Mather, Climatic classification for environmental biology. C. W. Thornthwaite Associates Laboratory of Climatology, Publications in Climatology 19, no. 4, Elmer, New Jersey.

MacMahon, J. A. 1979. North American deserts: their floral and faunal components, p. 21–82. In D. W. Goodall, R. A. Perry, and K. M. W. Howes, eds., Arid-land ecosystems: structure, functioning and management. International Biological Programme Volume 1, Cambridge University Press, Cambridge. 881 p.

McGinnies, William G. 1968. Appraisal of research on vegetation of desert environments, p. 381–474. In William G. McGinnies, Bram J. Goldman, and Patricia Paylore, eds., Deserts of the world: an appraisal of research into their physical and biological environments. University of Arizona Press, Tucson, Arizona. 788 p.

Montgomery, Stephen Jon. 1976. Rodent-habitat relationships in Great Basin desert shrub communities. Master's thesis. Utah State University. 74 p.

Naef, Weston J., and James N. Wood. 1975. Era of exploration: the rise of landscape photography in the American West, 1860–1885. New York Graphic Society, Boston. 260 p.

Nixon, Elray S. 1961. An ecological study of an exclosure in the mountain brush vegetation of the Wasatch Mountains, Utah. Master's thesis. Brigham Young University. 245 p.

————, and Earl M. Christensen. 1959. An ecological study of an exclosure in the mountain brush vegetation in the Wasatch Mountains, Utah. Proceedings of the Utah Academy of Sciences, Arts and Letters 36:182–183.

Noble, I. R., and R. O. Slatyer. 1977. Post-fire succession of plants in Mediterranean ecosystems, p. 27–36. In Harold A. Mooney and C. Eugene Conrad, Tech. Coords., Proceedings of the symposium on the environmental consequences of fire and fuel management in Mediterranean ecosystems. U.S. Forest Service General Technical Report WO–3. 498 p.

————, and R. O. Slatyer. 1980. The use of vital attributes to predict successional changes in plant communities subject to recurrent disturbances. Vegetatio 43:5–21.

Norton, Brien E. 1978. The impact of sheep grazing on long-term succesional trends in salt desert shrub vegetation of southwestern Utah, p. 610–613. In Donald N. Hyder, ed., Proceedings of the first international rangeland congress. Society for Range Management, Denver, Colorado. 742 p.

Pengelly, W. Leslie. 1976. Probable causes of the recent decline of mule deer in western U.S.—a summary, p. 129–134. In Gar W. Workman and Jessop B. Low, eds., Mule deer decline in the west, a symposium. College of Natural Resources, Utah State University. 134 p.

Pickford, G. W. 1932. The influence of continued heavy grazing and of promiscuous burning on spring-fall ranges in Utah. Ecology 13:159–171.

Piemeisel, Robert L. 1951. Causes affecting change and rate of change in a vegetation of annuals in Idaho. Ecology 32:53–72.

Popov, Boris Hewitt. 1949. The introduced fishes, game birds, and game and fur-bearing mammals of Utah. Master's thesis. Utah State Agricultural College. 197 p.

Ream, R. R. 1960. An ordination of the oak communities of the Wasatch Mountains. Master's thesis. University of Utah. 52 p.

————. 1963. The vegetation of the Wasatch Mountains, Utah and Idaho. Ph.D. dissertation. University of Wisconsin.

R.P.S.P. (Rephotographic Survey Project). 1979. Second view: a rephotographic survey. mimeo. 5 p.

Reveal, James L. 1979. Biogeography of the Intermountain Region, a speculative appraisal. Mentzelia 4:1–92.

Rice, Barbara, and Mark Westoby. 1978. Vegetative response of some Great Basin shrub communities protected against jackrabbits or domestic livestock. Journal of Range Management 31:28–34.

Roberts, N. Keith, and B. Delworth Gardner. 1964. Livestock and the public lands. Utah Historical Quarterly 32:285–300.

Sampson, A. W. 1925. The foothill-montane-alpine flora and its environment. Contributions of the U.S. National Herbarium 25:24–31.

Shantz, H. L. 1925. Plant communities in Utah and Nevada. Contributions of the U.S. National Herbarium 25:15–23.

————, and R. L. Piemeisel. 1940. Types of vegetation in Escalante Valley, Utah, as indicators of soil conditions. U.S.D.A. Technical Bulletin 713. 46 p.

Shreve, Forrest. 1942. The desert vegetation of North America. Botanical Review 8:195–246.

Skougard, Michael Grant. 1976. Vegetational response to

three environmental gradients in a salt playa near Goshen, Utah County, Utah. Master's thesis. Brigham Young University. 75 p.

Slatyer, R. O., ed. 1977. Dynamic changes in terrestrial ecosystems: patterns of change, techniques for study and applications to management. MAB Technical Notes 4:1–30.

Sneva, F. A. 1965. Cheatgrass yield and precipitation fluctuations, p. 27–29. In The Cheatgrass Symposium, Vale, Oregon.

Soil Conservation Survey. 1973. Map of the soils of Utah. Distributed with LeMoyne Wilson, Marvin E. Olsen, Theron B. Hutchings, Alvin R. Southard, and Austin J. Erickson. 1975. Soils of Utah. Utah State University Agricultural Experiment Station Bulletin 492, Logan, Utah. 94 p.

Spencer, D. A. 1964. Porcupine population fluctuations in past centuries revealed by dendrochronology. Journal of Applied Ecology 1:127–150.

Stewart, George, W. P. Cottam, and S. S. Hutchings. 1940. Influence of unrestricted grazing on northern salt desert plant associations in western Utah. Journal of Agricultural Research 60:289–316.

Stokes, Marvin A., and John H. Dieterich, Tech. Coords. 1980. Proceedings of the fire history workshop. October 20–24, Tucson, Arizona. U.S. Forest Service General Technical Report RM–81. 142 p.

Sussman, Aaron. 1973. The amateur photographers handbook. Thomas Y. Crowell, New York. 562 p.

Taylor, Charles E., and Richard E. Spurr. 1973. Aerial photographs in the National Archives. National Archives and Records Service, General Service Administration Special List No. 25. 106 p.

Tew, R. K. 1967. Soil moisture depletion by Gambel Oak in central Utah. U.S. Forest Service Research Note INT–74.

Tueller, Paul T., C. Dwight Beeson, Robin J. Tausch, Neil E. West, and Kenneth H. Rea. 1979. Pinyon-juniper woodlands of the Great Basin: distribution, flora, vegetal cover. U.S. Forest Service Research Paper INT–229. 22 p.

Turner, Raymond M., and Martin M. Karpiscak. 1980. Recent vegetation changes along the Colorado River between Glen Canyon Dam and Lake Mead, Arizona. U.S. Geological Survey Professional Paper 1132. 125 p.

Twain, Mark (Samuel L. Clemens). 1899. Roughing it. Harper and Brothers, New York, Vol. 1. 326 p.

United Nations Conference on Desertification. 1977. Desertification: an overview. August 29—September 9, 1977, Nairobi.

U.S. Bureau of Land Management. 1958–1979. Public Land Statistics. U.S. Government Printing Office, Washington, D.C.

———— (with photographs by Mike Gilkerson). 1980. Historical comparison photography, mountain foothills, Dillon Resource Area, Montana. U.S. Bureau of Land Management. Montana State Office, Billings, Montana. 120 p.

U.S. Forest Service. 1960–1979. National Forests Fire Report. U.S. Forest Service, Washington, D.C.

Vale, Thomas Randolph. 1973. The sagebrush landscape of the Intermountain West. Ph.D. dissertation. Unversity of California, Berkeley. 508 p.

Van Hulst, Robert. 1978. On the dynamics of vegetation: patterns of environmental and vegetational change. Vegetatio 38:65–75.

Vest, E. D. 1962. Biotic communities in the Great Salt Lake Desert. Institute of Environmental Biological Research and Epizoology Series No. 73. Division of Biological Science, University of Utah, Salt Lake City, Utah. 122 p.

Wadsworth, Nelson B. 1975. Through camera eyes. Brigham Young University Press. Provo, Utah. 180 p.

Wahl, E. W., and T. L. Lawson. 1970. The climate of the midnineteenth century United States compared to the current normal. Monthly Weather Review 98:259–265.

Walker, Don D. 1964. The cattle industry of Utah, 1850–1900: an historical profile. Utah Historical Quarterly 32:182–197.

West, Neil E. 1979a. Survival patterns of major perennials in salt desert shrub communities of southwestern Utah. Journal of Range Management 32:442–445.

————. 1979b. Basic synecological relationships of sagebrush-dominated lands in the Great Basin and the Colorado Plateau, p. 33–41. In The sagebrush ecosystem: a symposium. College of Natural Resources, Utah State University. 251 p.

————, and Juan Gasto. 1978. Phenology of the aerial portions of shadscale and winterfat in Curlew Valley, Utah. Journal of Range Management 31:43–45.

————, D. R. Cain, and G. F. Gifford. 1973. Biology, ecology, and renewable resource management of the pigmy conifer woodlands of western North America: a bibliography. Utah State University Agricultural Experiment Station Research Report 12. 36 p.

————, Robin J. Tausch, Kenneth H. Rea, and Paul T. Tueller. 1978. Phytogeographical variation within juniper-pinyon woodlands of the Great Basin. Great Basin Naturalist Memoirs 2:119–136.

Westoby, Mark. 1980. Elements of a theory of vegetation dynamics in arid rangelands. Israel Journal of Botany 28:169–194.

White, Peter S. 1979. Pattern, process, and natural disturbance in vegetation. Botany Review 45:229–299.

Wilcox, Richard B. 1977. Canopy influence as a factor in determining understory community composition. Master's thesis. Brigham Young University. 42 p.

Woodbury, A. M. 1947. Distribution of pigmy conifers in Utah and northeastern Arizona. Ecology 28:113–126.

————. 1955. Ecology of the Great Salt Lake Desert I. An annual cycle of the desert jackrabbit. Ecology 36:353–356.

Yoakum, James D. 1978. Managing rangelands for the American pronghorn antelope, p. 584–587. In Donald N. Hyder, ed., Proceedings of the First International Rangeland Congress, Society of Range Management, Denver, Colorado. 742 p.

Young, James A., and Jerry D. Budy. 1979. Historical use of Nevada's pinyon-juniper woodlands. Journal of Forest History 23:111–121.

_____, and Raymond A. Evans. 1978. Population dynamics after wildfires in sagebrush grasslands. Journal of Range Management 31:283–289.

_____, Raymond A. Evans, and Jack Major. 1971. Alien plants in the Great Basin. Journal of Range Management 24:194–201.

_____, Raymond A. Evans, and Paul T. Tueller. 1976. Great Basin plant communities—pristine and grazed, p. 187–215. *In* Robert Elston and Patricia Headrick, eds., Holocene environmental change in the Great Basin.

Nevada Archeological Survey Research Paper No. 6.

_____, Richard E. Eckert, Jr., and Raymond A. Evans. 1979. Historical perspectives regarding the sagebrush ecosystem, p. 1–13. *In* The sagebrush ecosystem: a symposium, College of Natural Resources, Utah State University. 251 p.

Zohner, Kelvin Davis. 1967. A guide to the biogeographic literature of Utah. Master's thesis. University of Utah. 83 p.

General Index

Plant Index